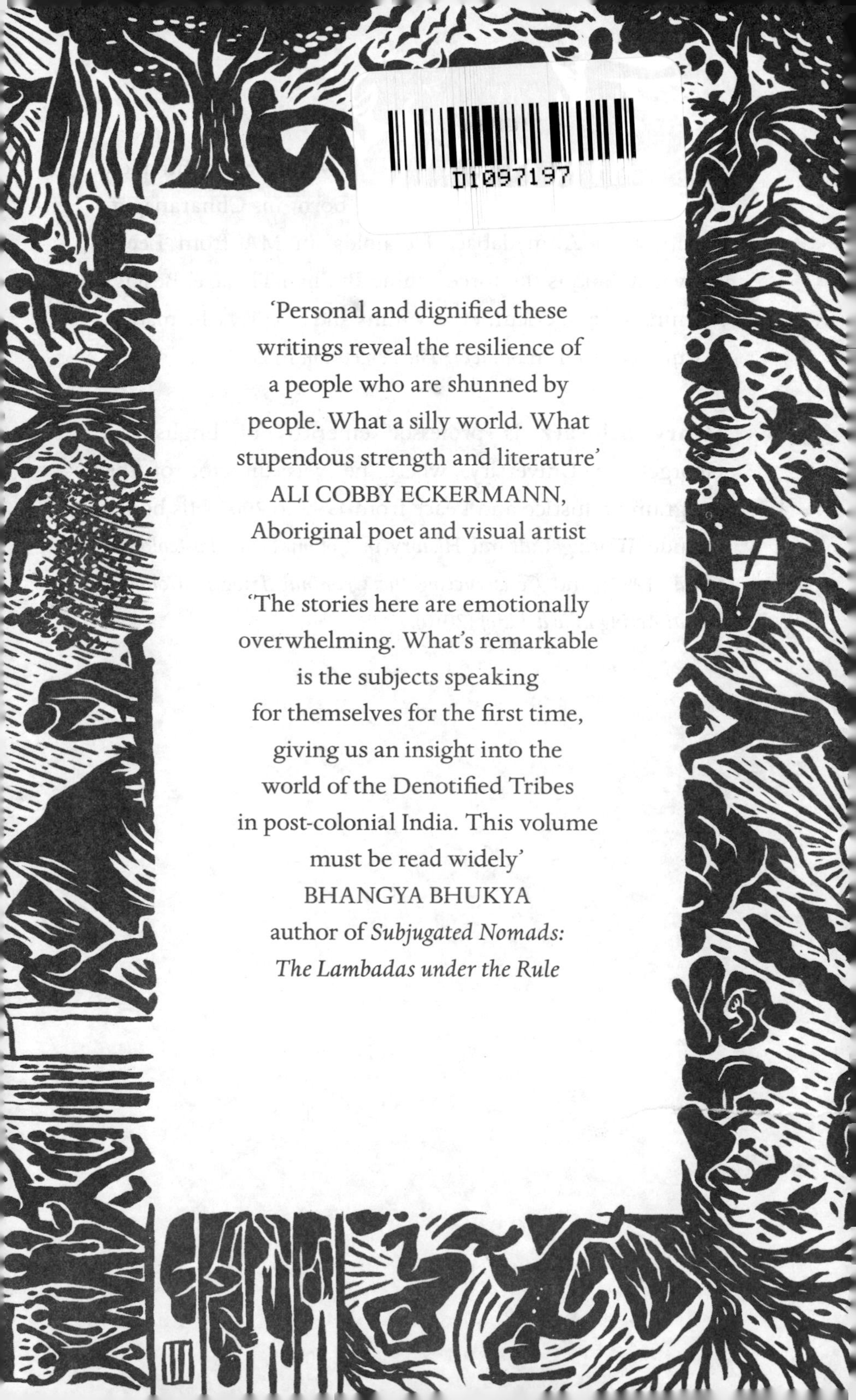



'Personal and dignified these writings reveal the resilience of a people who are shunned by people. What a silly world. What stupendous strength and literature'
ALI COBBY ECKERMANN,
Aboriginal poet and visual artist

'The stories here are emotionally overwhelming. What's remarkable is the subjects speaking for themselves for the first time, giving us an insight into the world of the Denotified Tribes in post-colonial India. This volume must be read widely'
BHANGYA BHUKYA
author of *Subjugated Nomads: The Lambadas under the Rule*

**Dakxin Bajrange** is an award-winning filmmaker, playwright, director and activist born in Chharanagar, a suburb of Ahmedabad. He holds an MA from Leeds University and is the force behind Budhan Theatre. Besides helming several documentary films and ten plays, he made a feature-length film *Sameer: The Perception* in 2017.

**Henry Schwarz** is professor emeritus of English at Georgetown University, where he was director of the Program on Justice and Peace from 1999 to 2007. His books include *Writing Cultural History in Colonial and Postcolonial India* (1997) and *Constructing the Criminal Tribe in Colonial India: Acting Like a Thief* (2010).

# VIMUKTA

*Freedom Stories*

To Stan,
For the future
— Henry

EDITED BY
**DAKXIN BAJRANGE**
**& HENRY SCHWARZ**

navayana

*Vimukta: Freedom Stories*

Edited by Henry Schwarz and Dakxin Bajrange

10 9 8 7 6 5 4 3 2 1

ISBN: 9788194865469

First published August 2021



See pages 186–7 for copyright acknowledgements

Navayana Publishing Pvt Ltd155 2nd Floor
Shahpur Jat, New Delhi 110049
Phone: +91-11-26494795
navayana.org

Typeset at Inosoft Systems, Noida

Printed by Sanjiv Palliwal, New Delhi

Distributed in South Asia by HarperCollins India

Subscribe to updates at navayana.org/subscribe
Follow on facebook.com/Navayana

# Contents

# Introduction

Henry Schwarz and Dakxin Bajrange

*Vimukta: Freedom Stories* is the first ever anthology of creative texts documenting the phenomenon of hereditary crime in postcolonial India. It contains primary accounts by those with a supposedly innate disposition to crime, written as creative reactions to their historical depictions.

The Indian experience is noteworthy as being the earliest, the largest, and perhaps the least-known experiment in modern social engineering around what Foucault famously called the carceral society.[1] From the early eighteenth-century categorization of ethnological types, to the early nineteenth-century discovery of organized thug bands roaming the highways, India has served as a repository for European notions of the dangerous and exotic. Learning to negotiate a multiplicity of languages, ethnicities, religions and customs, a wide range of Europeans, from employees of the East India Company to soldiers, missionaries and adventurers, created categories of human traits useful for the measurement and management of a diverse population that vastly outnumbered them. Definitions of who was within and who outside the British sphere of knowledge were crucial for comprehension, expansion and control. In the wake of the Revolt of 1857, such definitions hardened significantly, and with the takeover of the Company by the Crown in 1858, a proper imperial discipline was vigorously asserted. A little more than ten years after the suppression of the Revolt, a territory-wide census had been conducted, and definitions of which groups conformed to proper civilized behaviour were established, whether or not such groups had actively participated in fomenting rebellion. Many who did not conform to acceptable patterns of behaviour were labelled as criminal, and their ways of life were systematically suppressed towards the goal of administering a conquered territory.[2]

The icon of this label was the Criminal Tribes Act of 1871 (CTA), which defined some two hundred ethnic communities as 'addicted to the systematic commission of non-bailable offenses.' The Act called on district officials to 'notify' particular groups and individuals as fitting this definition, and then to register individuals as fitting the notification.

Registration entailed entering the name, aliases, domicile, distinguishing marks and other particulars in a police file. Registered persons were subject to roll call and a pass system that required them to take permission before leaving a village and upon entering another. The Act proposed a highly punitive brand of reformative government aimed at what it considered to be criminal lifestyles. Without defining exactly what 'crime' was, the CTA applied a rigorous military discipline towards communities said to be lazy, shiftless and idle. It did so in the name of fighting endemic sources of crime, which was thought to lie within the hereditary biology of the population. In this respect, it represented an early form of eugenics that had yet to develop a scientific basis. Its empirical evidence was the anthropological and criminological observations of district officials schooled in the suppression of the thug menace during the 1830s, now applied to the violent outbreak of the Revolt. Like so many Indian behaviours, crime could be explained by the hereditary principle of caste; and since caste was said to be immutable, and determined how all descendants would practice their traditional occupations, it only seemed logical that crime, too, was an inherited and unalterable profession.

The Act was extraordinary in several respects. For one, it was among the earliest legal instruments that had territory-wide jurisdiction, demonstrating the Crown's confidence in its sovereignty over its annexed and now subdued territory. The CTA was debated by the most senior officials in the new British Raj, and for its day represented the farthest-reaching effort at social control imposed within a militarily conquered territory. Notable both for its all-India application and for the personnel who debated it, the Act outlined and defined a coherent, if contradictory, ideology of rule that would characterize British dominance for the next seventy-five years. This ideology stressed absolute military control while experimenting around the edges with newly-emerging European strains of utilitarian and liberal political thought. The Act itself directly intended to stamp out what were considered systematic and hereditary crimes such as Thuggee, and in the process to 'civilize' large populations of mostly nomadic tribals by counting, containing, and eventually settling them in fixed abodes.

This process of taming the wild, wandering tribespeople, besides suppressing illegal activity, was to have an ennobling effect as well. An enlightened ruler of a country and its people ought at minimum to guarantee law and order; having attained that goal, the benevolent despot could extend the hand of correction and rehabilitation as much as of punishment and control. Oscillating between asserting authority on the one hand, and freeing the benighted subject from the shackles of tradition on the other, the 'authoritarian liberalism' promoted by the Act offered nomads a graduation into colonial enlightenment. While destroying their way of life, it provided the civilizing benefits of the jail and the whip.

The Act proposed a highly punitive brand of reformative government aimed at what it defined as criminal lifestyles. Without defining exactly what crime was, nor how exactly it was handed down between generations, the 1871 CTA applied a rigorous military discipline towards communities said to be shiftless. Initial provisions of the Act made notification uncontestable in any court of justice; wandering tribes that refused to settle could be forcibly relocated and sedantized; they could additionally be placed in reformatory settlements. Further iterations of the Act in 1911 and 1924 placed additional constraints on the populations, requiring their fingerprinting, removal of their children to borstal reformatories, and repeat offender provisions that could have the suspect transported across the kala paani. The former penal colony at Port Blair, Andaman Islands, still houses freed Bantu speaking inmates who had been transported to the penitentiary in the early twentieth century.

While aimed at countering perceived threats to the social

order by stamping out the 'criminal way of life' that might sow the seeds of a further rebellion, the Act also served a pedagogical function by promoting a particularly British vision of what India should look like, extolling the benefits of settled village agriculture over those of nomadism, and the virtues of hard work over the allegedly lazy lifestyles of groups who had migrated and wandered for centuries. Those whose ways of life were deemed most dangerous included nomads and travellers of many types: shepherds, itinerant musicians, dramatic performers and acrobats, minstrels, astrologers and genealogists, holy men, saints and philosophers and a great variety of legitimate tradespeople and carriers who brought skills and commodities from village to village and from sea coasts to central regions, such as the Banjaras who carried ocean salt to the hinterlands.

The occupations of many of these groups had begun to be significantly affected by the construction of railways since the 1850s. After the Revolt, India was to be a sedentary, rural, agricultural, unchanging, and most importantly, tax-paying place, one connected, moreover, by regulated commerce, observing government monopolies on commodities like salt and opium, and traveling on approved transportation lines. Wanderers came under suspicion for the many languages they spoke and the potentially subversive information they carried. Combined with the Forest Acts of 1865 and 1878, vesting sole proprietary power over forest produce to the new government, the ancient lifeways and resource patterns of vast groups became untenable. The 1911 and 1924 versions of the CTA called for wider and deeper implementation of its provisions. As enthusiasm grew for systematic administration, more elaborate schemes were developed for the management of India's subaltern populations. Where resources permitted, settlements were established to concentrate notified groups into secure enclaves. Especially in the Punjab, where officials were posted who had trained under the arch-Thug marauder, William Sleeman, whole villages had been declared criminal warrens and cordoned with barbed wire and constant surveillance since the 1850s. Eventually, an archipelago of reformatory settlements was constructed that soon housed upwards of fifty thousand persons annually. When the Act was finally repealed in 1952, 2.3 million tribals were allegedly decriminalized. But not for long. Within a very short time, the police forces in state after state had them successfully recriminalized under habitual offender statutes.

During the first decades of the twentieth century, the Salvation Army launched a spirited campaign to contain the incorrigibles in hardened reformatories, correcting the 'rabbit warren approach'. The Army was granted its first criminal settlement in 1908 in Bengal, and by the 1930s both government and charitable agencies such as the Army were administering some fifty settlements throughout the country. While there was never any comprehensive census of criminal tribe populations, whether in or outside settlements, the most notorious of them such as Solapur in Maharashtra consistently housed upwards of two thousand persons annually over a period of forty years. Ranging from small, isolated outposts in jungles to concentration camp-like, industrial cities of captive labour, the settlements provided cheap, disciplined workers to eager employers who promised to further school them in the rigours of agricultural or industrial toil.[3]

Criminal tribesmen and women performed the hardest, dirtiest and most dangerous jobs: manning the steam-powered spinning mills of Bombay and Ahmedabad; operating the drying engines in the tobacco factory at Stuartpuram; laying railroad tracks; excavating mines and coalfields; digging canals; baking bricks; building roads and bridges; cultivating and harvesting in the opium, tea and fruit plantations. Where gainful employment could not be provided by private employers, the demands of rehabilitation kept settlers occupied in free labour for the Empire: clearing forests, draining wetlands, grading roads, cutting sleepers, crushing stone. Oliver Harold Baptist Starte, officer of the Backwards Classes Department of Bombay Presidency during the 1920s and 1930s, a champion of enlightened reform of these populations through education and labour, records a settlement of criminal tribes at the Nira Project engaged in 'digging sand from the creek', presumably to create a canal. One account records the use of settlement labour as 'cat's paws' for breaking wasteland into cultivable soil; another cites the use of this 'vast reserve army' as scabs and strike-breakers when militant workers organized in resistance to management demands.[4]

British police officials, Christian missionaries and Hindu and Muslim charitable agencies kept records of this activity, some quite detailed, yet till date this information is not collected in a central repository. While many official reports, government commissions, formal enquiries and scholarly studies exist in the archives of British India, the bulk of data and statistics lie unnoticed in district archives, police stations and other locations where it may still remain unclassified. What is available in the repositories of colonial correspondence, such as the India Office Library, are scattered and almost incidental reports of commissions long ago forgotten, whose cumulative effect provides only a fraction of the evidence needed to begin the proper historical reconstruction of this vanished chapter of history.[5] Interestingly, the Salvation Army still proudly displays its history of rehabilitation of the criminal tribes on its various websites, and in an organization much given to self-promotion, this is considered one of its greatest achievements.

Recognizing this history is a crucial task if we are to come to grips with the reality of India's past and the lingering prejudice that continues to structure social life today. It is even more urgent for the tens of millions of descendants of these interned tribespeople, some of whom may still not recognize the rationale for their continued victimization by the police, to recover their history. Till today, the police academies, such as the facility at Karai, Gandhinagar, include in their syllabi mandatory chapters about the incorrigible nature of the born criminal castes and tribes, and the necessity to subdue them by force, often using torture and incarceration as appropriate techniques.

As the movement to win liberation for this population has emerged and gathered strength over the last twenty years, one point of progress has been to re-educate the police by revising their syllabus and encouraging a revaluation of this brutal legacy. Some enlightened administrators have been receptive to this task. Yet Indian society at large still labours under the received idea, perpetuated since early British times, of an enormous criminal underclass that opportunistically feeds off the average, law-abiding citizen. Popular culture has dutifully reflected this disposition. Blockbusters from *Gunga Din* (1933) to *Indiana Jones and the Temple of Doom* (1984) periodically resuscitate the lurid blood sacrifice at the altar of Kali Ma, and Aamir Khan and Amitabh Bachchan's *Thugs of Hindostan* (2017) is but one in a long line of repetitions.

From the mythical fear whipped up by the colonial police during the 1830s of a macabre, genetically driven race of marauding thugs, law enforcement till today perpetuates a high-stakes game of racial profiling and guilt by association. Hidden in the darkness of non-history, the perpetuation of the myth of innate criminality is lucrative business. Although successive governments over the last twenty years have begun to recognize this history, and have recently convened a new commission within the Ministry of Social Justice and Empowerment, there is no single, official account of this saga, and still no serious attempt to make restitution or even afford official recognition. This volume marks one small effort in that direction.[6]

Official corruption in India is legion. The police actively participate in a vicious cycle of circular or ordinary crime, preying on those who were once marginalized by the colonial authority. The areas around the former settlements were developed as places of rehabilitation or 'free colonies,' often under the watchful eye of a police surveillance post. When the settlements were disbanded between the 1930s and the 1950s, inmates were released into these free colonies, frequently without any education or vocational training.

Such ghettos of released inmates tend to continue to be crime-laden. The phenomenon is at least double-edged: people debarred from good employment and respectable social status, not to mention housing, education and health care, tended to commit petty crimes as a means of subsistence. Like all vulnerable populations, their mere existence can stretch the limits of the acceptable. Yet the police too understand a preponderance for crime as a business opportunity. As a character in the documentary video *Acting Like a Thief* (2006) declares: 'The police are our good friends. We've been doing business together for more than a hundred years.'[7] Upon their release from settlements on 31 August 1952, individual states reclassified the now 'Denotified' and nomadic tribals as 'habitual offenders'. So the cycle continues.

Take for example Chharanagar, the free colony into which inmates of the Ahmedabad Settlement, administered by the Salvation Army from 1930, were released. Chharanagar today is a thug's paradise, where roughly fifty per cent of the resident families brew country liquor under the eye of the police. Many of the other families are engaged in games of chance, such as numbers, dice and cards. Insurance deception schemes engage many, as does prostitution, bootlegging and smuggling. Among the most lucrative schemes is the filing of false charges by the police against suspected criminals, or 'persons of questionable character', who must answer charges against them based on secret evidence. The existence of emergency legislations such as the Prevention of Anti-Social Activities Act (PASA) affords the police the authority to continually intimidate suspects into paying bribes to avoid prosecution and jail time. Many default to incarceration when the bribe is exorbitant. Protection is a full-time profession. Strikingly, Chharanagar boasts an enormous density of legal professionals, many of whom are employed in defending community members against false cases. Such cases can drag on for years in India's sclerotic legal system, and the combined pressure of police extortion and legal limbo drives many to bankruptcy. In the long run, it is easier to pay the bribe.

Stigmatized populations are sensitive to pressure, and research has shown that the police are a large motivator for the commission of crime, turning a blind eye to a bribe, or actively encouraging, inciting or compelling illegal activity in order to profit from it. The threat of coercion convinces 'born criminals' to follow illegal pursuits in fear of a beating or the lock-up. The police take a large cut of the profits from illegal activity either as protection money or as direct beneficiaries of fenced goods, and so crime is systematic and normalized to mutual benefit. Communities that have been criminalized historically learn new methods of existence over time. If they had not been traditional brewers of liquor, they become so under changing needs and circumstances, such as confinement in settlements or being housed in states under prohibition, such as Gujarat. Their experience in transporting goods became useful in making objects appear or disappear.

The settlements were breeding grounds for the innovation of unique technical skills when the old ways were suddenly shut off. Former nomads now catered to the needs of the sedentary, especially as they fell out of line with traditional norms of settled life. The free colonies to a certain extent became havens for free expression: as in many gypsy communities the world over, outsiders come into the ghetto at night to experience its exoticism and relaxed morality. They leave before dawn having had their fill, perhaps paying a police bribe, and returning to their respectable families, no questions asked. If there was trouble, the police would round up the usual suspects.

Budhan Theatre explains, 'We are not born thieves, we are born actors.' Yet thieving is its own form of dramatic performance, frequently involving the orchestration of several members engaged in various roles, such as camaraderie, diversion, lookout, bribery and getaway, among others. Among the most unique and potentially effective techniques for survival has been the creation and evolution of a body of creative expression that gives voice to the criminal experience. This expression, with some older roots, really only began to flourish in 1998 with the play *Budhan*, which is included in this volume, produced in street theatre style (bhawai). Written, directed and performed collectively by Budhan Theatre, this play helped to put the pressing needs of the criminalized communities on the map. We will return to the contemporary cultural landscape, but first a sketch of the extraordinary but still unknown story of wide scale criminality and criminalization in colonial British India.[8]

Historical documents illustrate the early colonial construction of the hereditary criminal as a problem for military and social administration. Legislative Acts codified genetic criminality as the law of the land which birthed the reformatory regime that attempted to control and correct the 'criminal impulse' as a problem of social management.

This volume's most original contribution is to raise the voices of the oppressed criminal populations who have been subjected to a century and a half of systematic oppression. Allegedly 'born criminals' speak in these pages, telling their first-hand stories for the first time. Reacting against an historical legacy of oppression, these contemporary storytellers bear witness to the historical experience of their ancestors, and point us towards an uncertain but hopeful future. Stories come from all regions of the Indian subcontinent, with translations from Marathi, Hindi, Gujarati, Telugu, Bantu and Narsi-Parsi (thieves' argot), illustrating the fabric of DNT life in India today.

II

Prior to the invention of modern, scientific anthropology, police forces on the frontier of Empire were encountering exotic others and learning to interact. A narrative took hold in central India, near today's Bhopal, in the early decades of the nineteenth century, that organized bands of marauders were murdering travellers on the highways. These gangs, known as thugs or thuggees (from Sanskrit thak, or deceiver), or alternately as phansigars (from Persian phansi or noose), became an obsession for one Captain William Henry Sleeman, who devoted his entire career to combatting this scourge.

Sleeman is regarded as among the chief proponents for the assertion of British power in a previously unregulated territory, Saugor and Narbudda, which he accomplished through a concerted public relations campaign centred around the alleged depredations of the murderous thugs. The undercurrent of Sleeman's campaign implies that by suppressing the thugs, British sovereignty would prove its benevolence; and although he does not state so explicitly, it is nonetheless clear that by exaggerating their horrendousness, the legitimacy of Company Raj rose in inverse proportion to the threat. Crime fighting became a metaphor and a justification for territorial acquisition; pacification of a terrorist threat entitled the peace keeper to his new-earned lands.

As the East India Company extended its sway from mercantile trading to military conquest, British notions of law and order encountered greater and more lurid threats to their sovereignty, which it sought to manage and contain. By most accounts the Revolt caught the Company unawares. In its wake, vast swathes of the population became suspect and required surveillance. Sleeman's agents in Bhopal in the 1830s became the next generation of policing officials on the western frontier, especially in the Punjab and the North-Western Frontier Province, where they began to discover threats to security practically everywhere. Sleeman's 1839 text, *History of the Thugs or Phansigars of India*, to which is frequently appended in subsequent reprints his earlier *Ramaseeana, or A Vocabulary of the Peculiar Language Used by the Thugs* (1836) became the blueprint for subsequent would-be thug hunters in the police forces, much repeated in later years.

Evidence of this is found in James Hutton's *Popular Account of the Thugs and Dacoits: The Hereditary Garroters and Gang-Robbers of India* (1857). To a very great extent Hutton's

*Account* is precisely that: it merely repeats Sleeman's earlier account. Indeed Sleeman's book itself copies verbatim, as its first thirty-five pages, the prior account of one Richard Sherwood, who penned "Of the Murderers called Phansigars" in 1816. Thus to a large extent Sleeman's is already a textual repetition, based around language as evidence and prior sources as history, including even Herodotus, the fifth century BCE Greek 'father of history' (who is equally renowned to be the 'father of lies'). Indeed Hutton, writing twenty years after Sleeman, opens his account with the direct reference to Herodotus and the assertion that the Thugs had been practicing their dastardly craft since time immemorial. Countless other manuals, handbooks, textbooks and primers entered the market, designed primarily for police training, but also capitalizing on the large audience for pulp crime fiction and ripping tales from the tropics. The thug story—as story—quickly became a stock genre, a trope of the thrills and dangers of adventure in the Empire.

An entire volume could be written about this canon, but it would soon become highly repetitive, because nearly every subsequent account lays down the well-worn outlines of Sleeman's story (who himself took it from Sherwood). Nonetheless it became stock-in-trade of the Indian police to understand this lore and to inculcate it in its cadres. Thus the Police Handbook became a prime source for perpetuating the thrilling story of the thuggee, whatever its veracity. New ranks of cadets sought to make their fame by ferreting out new gangs, new conspiracies—which looked exactly like the old gangs—and through the post-Revolt period ever more communities were notified—put on notice—that their allegedly illegal activities had been discovered and were to be curtailed. These stories are still continually repeated in today's Indian press. Hollywood reanimated the tale in *Indiana Jones and the Temple of Doom*, and a recent journalistic account by British historian Mike Dash (2005) repeats the stereotype with remarkably little scepticism. Indian newspapers endlessly recycle the myth of habitual criminals making their seasonal rounds of the major towns. This is not to say that organized, hereditary crime does not exist, but that its literary representation through recognizable tropes and narratives has evolved into a peculiar institution over a century and a half due to a variety of historical forces, not least among them the legal declaration of hereditary criminality itself, the complex network of pseudo-scientific discourses that sustain it, the complicity of a sensationalist media, and the attendant social stigma that passes as common sense.[9]

A next phase in the story of habitual crime is that of reform, indeed redemption. When the Salvation Army entered the criminal tribe arena in the early twentieth century, Commissioner Frederick St. George de Latour Booth-Tucker, son-in-law of the Army's founder William Booth, deemed the government's policy for administering criminals to be incoherent, and he proposed a solution. 'Criminocurology' would apply the scientific principles of 'Concentration, Control, Employment and Reform' to some 3,300 inhabitants in twenty-three settlements throughout India, numbers soon to be doubled. Booth-Tucker's 1912 tract by that name is fascinating as much for its exuberant language as for its historical centrality.

Tucker himself was an Anglo-Indian, born in Monghyr (Munger in present-day Bihar), and as such was personally motivated to redeem himself in the eyes of respectable British society in the colony. But this was not to be so, even after marrying General Booth's daughter; Salvationists in general were viewed with suspicion, as an extremist cult so bent on evangelism and conversion that they threatened the peace by arousing religious animosities. Indeed, only the dregs of society were to be trusted to them, and so government viewed their solution to the crime problem as expedient but strictly limited.

Booth-Tucker was a flamboyant if not somewhat ludicrous figure, adopting native dress and walking barefoot over hot sands. His enthusiasm for the work is mirrored in his prose; with hyperbole bordering on the rapturous, he described the 'state of war' engaged by the habitual criminals: '[A] compact phalanx of trained warriors.… They meet power with cunning, and force with fraud.… Trained from infancy by their expert leaders, they carry on a guerilla warfare which defies the combined efforts of an army of 150,000 police and 700,000 village watchmen to repress.' His programme of rehabilitation was fairly simple: prayer and labour. The 'Gospel of Compulsion' would be nothing short of miraculous. Booth-Tucker wrote of the Stuartpuram settlement, citing Isaiah: 'The desert shall rejoice and blossom as the rose. It shall blossom abundantly, and rejoice even with joy and singing.'[10]

Government reports on the success or failure of these experiments were mixed. Rather than redeem the Army from official suspicion, the agencies responsible for their oversight, while grateful for their financial assistance in subduing this difficult population, found that settlements were more interested in conversion than in producing productive workers. Indeed some were reported to be acting more as Christian reformatories than as self-supporting labour camps.

Booth-Tucker and his wife spent their time amongst the Depressed Classes in India until their transfer to the United States and Catherine's untimely death there in 1903, at which point he returned to India to complete his life's work in earnest. He developed a passion for settling criminal tribes while searching for ways to expand the Army's ranks of captive souls; his 1923 publication *Mukti Fauj* summarizes his forty years' experience 'taming the Crim'. *Criminocurology* is an early manifesto of the Army's willingness to intervene in government policy at a time when it was especially receptive to parsimonious solutions.

Indeed the turning over of a despised and brutalized population to the agency of an evangelical religious missionary outfit heralds an early version of neoliberalism, as we have seen in the late twentieth and early twenty-first centuries, with its mercenary paramilitaries and disaster relief crews farming out the business of state. Meena Radhakrishna's historical account of the descendants of the Stuartpuram Settlement in Andhra Pradesh, *Dishonoured by History: 'Criminal Tribes' and British Colonial Policies* (2001), is a fascinating study of the dependency consciousness of people raised to internalize their flawed condition and to constantly strive for their Christian redemption in a condition of abject poverty and unrelenting toil.[11]

On the government side, Mr O.H.B. Starte is an appropriate representative, having served as the Backwards Class Officer of Bombay Presidency for over twenty-five years. In meticulously detailed records for the government authority, as well as in several monographs devoted to delinquency and reformation of juveniles, Starte painted graphically the reality of the settlement experience. In Starte's *Annual Administrative Reports* resides the stark reality of social control in 'liberal' British India in the twentieth century. In Bombay Presidency alone, his *Report* for 1934 contains precise statistics on the fifteen criminal tribe settlements and five 'special institutions' run by the government there, along with the fourteen free colonies into which inmates were released under police surveillance. He details the daily activities of the 8,123 residents of the settlements, and the 6,761 residents of the free colonies. Interestingly, Starte's *Reports* also records the growth of Dharavi as a free colony in the early 1930s, a place that has earned the reputation of being one of the world's largest slums.[12]

Since Bombay Presidency was one of four presidencies at the time (Bengal, Madras, and the North-Western Provinces comprising the others), one can begin to extrapolate a population roughly four times as large throughout the subcontinent, and that only held in government facilities as opposed to other reforming agencies such as the Salvation Army, Hindu Mahasabha, Arya Samaj, Chief Khalsa Diwan, Anjuman-I-Islamia and others. Of course the criminal tribes institutions by presidency were not proportional, based on a variety of factors, but rough statistics show about eighty thousand people physically interned on presumption of hereditary criminality in 1935; by the time of independence in 1947, many millions of nationalist agitators would be added to the count of incarcerated persons in India's jails and prisons, on a model suggested by Sandria Freitag to have followed that of the CTA. But the freedom fighters were released from jail after independence and granted pensions and hero status, while the Denotified tribes had to wait until 1952 to partake of independence, and till today do not enjoy the privileges and responsibilities of full citizenship.

Sher Singh 'Sher' was the first member of his community to write a volume on the historical and sociological conditions of the nomadic Sansi tribe. His 1965 study, *Sansis of the Punjab: A Gypsy and Denotified Tribe*, is an extraordinary, multidisciplinary account of the Sansi ethnos, tracing their history and genealogy back to the Delhi Sultanate (c. 1550), and then forward into the denotified, Nehruvian, socialist present. Relentlessly optimistic, Sher is among the first authentic writers from his community to bring a participant's perspective to the conundrum of hereditary crime. He is perhaps among the first to be educated to the post-graduate level. The chapter titled "Criminal Tribes Act and the Sansis," from his 1965 work, may be the first social scientific, non-governmental study of the effect of the successive Acts on the incarcerated population. It is a measured, sober analysis of the deficits of the wandering communities during an era of modernization, as well as an assessment of the effects of incarceration and rehabilitation, that concludes: 'Today the Sansis are free and respectable citizens of India, having all the rights and responsibilities like any other citizen. Now they can go anywhere, do anything for improving themselves and their children. Now they will transmit to their children a freedom which is the indispensable requisite for the proper and full development of a nation.' Sher's next chapter, "National Government and De-Notified Tribes Including Sansis" (not included here) details the expenses allotted by the independent government of India for the social uplift of the criminal groups during its first three five-year plans. It calls to mind a famous statement attributed to Sarojini Naidu about the founder of the nation, Mahatma Gandhi: 'He had no idea how expensive it was for the people to enable him to live in poverty.'

Colonial British India has been called the laboratory of mankind by Bernard Cohn. In itself, the experience of European contact records the growth of the modern social and natural sciences, many of which were stimulated by the remarkable diversity and variety of life found there. It can equally be considered the laboratory of social engineering, where literally hundreds of millions of people were eliminated due to famine, reconstituted in their identities, and reshuffled across borders in the partitions that were the price of independence.[13]

By the time of India's independence in 1947, the number of alleged born criminals stood at some three to four million, or about ten per cent of the population. In 2018, seventy years after independence, the percentage of descendants of these born criminals still stigmatized by the legacy of their past remains the same. The rough number used by activists is a hundred million.

Independence resulted in the eventual de-criminalization of this vast population, but more in name than in deed.

'Denotified' as criminals by prime minister Nehru on 31 August 1952, the former criminal tribes were quickly re-criminalized under a series of habitual offender statutes in various states. Rebranded as Denotified and Nomadic Tribes (or Vimukta Jatis in Hindi, DNTs in English), this legislative Frankenstein's monster has nowhere found a home under India's constitutional provisions.

The various ethnic communities gathered under the DNT label, while to a large extent Adivasi in origin, have been classified under each of the three constitutional schedules in different states, and sometimes as under different categories within the same state depending on region. So for example the Sansi tribals who today identify as the Chhara people of Ahmedabad, Gujarat, were in the mid-nineteenth century nomads wandering the semi-arid barrens of Saurashtra, Northern Punjab and Western Rajasthan. Having been settled in the Ahmedabad reformatory in the 1930s, the Chharas of that district are today labelled as Other Backward Classes (OBCs), while in neighbouring Maninagar the Sansi population there is labelled as a Scheduled Caste (SC), and in Panch Mahals district as a Scheduled Tribe (ST). Each of these groups considers the other Sansis as kin within an extended endogamous group, eligible for marriage and membership in the tribal panchayat. And yet the state-wide census enumerates each group as distinct, and so no pan-Gujarati Sansi identity of any consequence can mobilize to agitate for constitutional provision. Due to such fragmentation and lack of political representation, the Denotified Sansis remain playthings of the authorities, regularly hounded for bribes, thrown into lockups, beaten for confessions, and forced into a life of petty illegality. That is changing.

For the last twenty years we have seen flicker into life a nascent movement for the civil rights of these wrongly accused groups, who, like convicted felons the world over, have few rights to housing, education, health care, or representative democracy. The government of independent India has attempted some small measure of redress, first in its decriminalization of the tribes, and then its appointment of various committees of enquiry to study the issue and to propose recommendations, as it has done since independence. The movement to secure civil rights for the DNTs over the last fifteen years has been successful in achieving the appointment of a national commission within the Ministry of Social Justice and Empowerment. Yet this commission has accomplished precisely nothing, and its leadership has been staffed by political appointees with a vested interest in accomplishing less than nothing. The spearhead of the movement has not been constitutional reform but popular activism, with various groups taking to cultural production and public performance to voice their grievances and build awareness among the general population. The vanguard intellectuals who have launched and sustained the movement included Mahasweta Devi, G.N. Devy and Laxman Gaikwad. The younger generations of cultural activists, led by Kanji Patel and Dakxin Bajrange, are featured in this volume.

## III

This collection presents the voices of marginalized communities some one hundred and fifty years on from their systematic criminalization. The nine texts collected here are far from comprehensive, but rather form a snapshot of the experience of being branded a hereditary criminal in independent India. These voices, from different regions, languages and cultures of the subcontinent, speak to the existential reality of living under the colonial hangover of alleged criminality. Despite their differences, each highlights the experience of crime and its enormous shaping role in defining identity and the possibilities of living today. The selections are arranged in no particular order, but each is contemporary, composed by living artists to describe his or her world. They include oral testimony recorded and translated into English by a professional ethnographer or a community activist; written autobiography; personal reflection; three dramatic play scripts; and an excerpt from a novel. From among the vast range of DNT utterances, this is what we have collected in English. It is due to the honour and integrity of the translators and collectors that we have this material at all. Most of all, it is due to the passion and heartfelt desire to speak by their creators that we have these remarkable stories in the first place.

Dakxin Kumar Bajrange Chhara (b. 1971) is a prime mover, with others, of the collective dramatic ensemble, Budhan Theatre. Much more than a performance group, Budhan's activities include a library, an after-school literacy centre and community outreach and organizing of many kinds, from displacement of transient populations, alternate employment schemes, improving police relations, to organizing and advocacy through government agencies on behalf of DNTs. Based in a northern suburb of Ahmedabad,

Dakxin's grandparents were released from the infamous settlement of that name in the 1930s into a free colony in which virtually the entire community still lives, a gypsy ghetto of unimproved housing without paved roads, and tenuous water and electricity. Chharanagar is a notorious neighborhood where even taxis do not venture. It is a hotbed for bootlegging and for brewing country liquor (daru), and as such is a place both attractive and despised for the citizens of Gujarat, a dry state.

Immediately after the murder of Budhan Sabar by the police in February 1998, eminent writer and activist Mahasweta Devi formed an Action Group with esteemed literary critic G.N. Devy and novelist and politician Laxman Gaikwad. All were winners of the Sahitya Akademi award, and Mahasweta at that time had garnered the Magsaysay Award and the Padma Shri, India's foruth-highest civilian honour. The group set out to visit the most oppressed communities in India, and discovered Chharanagar. After relating Budhan's story to the residents, Budhan Theatre was formed. The Action Group donated a library to the community. This became the focal point for the Theatre's activities.

Budhan Theatre's first production, *Budhan*, penned by Dakxin Bajrange Chhara, graphically captured the arrest, torture and killing of Budhan Sabar in 1998, the event that launched the DNT movement in its contemporary phase. Several of the original actors in *Budhan* have gone on to win national scholarships and theatrical celebrity. There have been several hundred performances of *Budhan* since its first showing. It has been translated into Gujarati, English, Hindi and Malayalam, but nothing compares to the rawness of the original dialogues. The play is the final chapter of this anthology.

Dakxin's two other contributions to this volume include a section from his autobiography, *Budhan Speaks* (*Budhan Bolta Hai*) and the script of a play about the removal of pavement dwellers, *Bulldozer*. The autobiography won the National Human Rights Award in 2010. Both the pieces were written in Hindi and have been translated into English by Sonal, a long-time employee of the Bhasha Research and Publication Centre in Vadodara. The autobiography has not been published previously in English.

Kushal Batunge (b. 1998) is a college graduate in Ahmedabad. Also from Chharanagar, he is the child of a family of bootleggers and an actor of the second generation of Budhan Theatre. He has learned filmmaking by attending community workshops and currently organizes a very popular weekly film screening series at the Chharanagar library. His narrative piece, "Who Am I?" lies somewhere between autobiography, testimony and meditation on his particular situation in the present place and time. It is a moving personal reflection about growing up in an environment of endemic police harassment and the toll it exacts on families.

Eminent DNT rights activist Subba Rao Mali Rao (b. 1955) from Telangana has provided a fascinating piece of ethnographic fieldwork from a DNT couple. Pativada Satya Narayana and P. Chinni (birthdates unknown) narrate how their lives have been coloured by the scourge of criminality, and how they eke out a living as members of the formerly nomadic Mondi Banda and Dasari communities. The Mondi Banda are traditional collectors of honey from beehives, which are usually located high in trees and cliffs, requiring climbing skills. Dasaris are collectors of human hair, and sellers of cosmetics and personal toiletries. The harrowing stories of this couple, who are forced to move to the city as the jungle erodes behind them, and then the city overwhelms them, are representative of a generation in the 1970s and 80s when unchecked urbanization displaced millions of rural DNTs and swallowed them into urban poverty with few employment, education, or housing options. Their consequent hardships and skills of survival are both tragic and inspirational. Subba Rao has translated the account from Telugu to English.

Professor Kanji Patel (b. 1952) is a well-known regional writer in Gujarati language from the Panch Mahals district, a hilly, tribal region where three states come together in astonishing linguistic and cultural diversity. He is the author of the novellas *Kotar ni Dhar Par* (1982), *Dahelu* (1989) and *Aadi* (2008). *Dero* is his collection of short stories about DNTs (2008). His collections of poetry are *Janpada* (1991), *Dungardev* (2006) and *Dharti na Vachan* (2012). He has won awards for his writings and activism. His works have been translated into English, Marathi, Hindi, Assamese and Bengali. His novel *Dahelu* has been published in English as *Rear Verandah* (1997) by Macmillan India. His original contribution to this volume, *Pata,* is a collection of three dramatic scenarios—"Mahabharat," "Land," and "Railroad Tracks"—that details how DNTs today are regularly hounded off their land, beaten on suspicion and cheated by their superiors. It has been translated into English by Rupali Burke and published here for the first time.

*Pata* was first performed in Gujarati by Budhan Theatre at the Gujarat Vidyapith (Gujarat Gandhian University) in February 2015. This was in fact Budhan Theatre's first attempt at performance in Gujarati, a language by which it is surrounded, but with which the community does not directly engage. It addresses this question of multiple jurisdictions, multiple incomprehensions, as well as the daily struggle of DNTs just to survive. Thus the specific logistics of the performance itself act out the central dynamic of the play, in which the final scene shows members of three distinct DNT communities coming together to destroy the railroad tracks that symbolically mark the devastation of their traditional ways of life, promoting a vibrant solidarity.

The popular Gujarati writer, Dhruv Bhatt (b. 1947), is the author of nine novels and two collections of poetry. A winner of the Sahitya Akademi award at both the state and national levels, his 2015 novel *Timirpanthi* (*Children of Darkness*) is here presented in an original translation by Vishal Bhadani. Dhruv did extensive research for this novel by talking to the Chharas, among others, about their daily lives and the modus operandi of their illegal activities. It shows a profound understanding of the criminal mind in both the tactics of thieving and the psychology of the thief. The first two chapters presented here illustrate the simultaneous cunning and simplicity of people termed as 'hereditary criminals'. Guileless Saraswati (ironically named for the goddess of learning) embodies perfectly the matter-of-factness that marks the criminal identity: 'She accepts responsibility for whatever she does. She would fake it, dramatize and do whatever she feels is right, but she would neither pretend to reject it nor gloss it over with lies. Sati would admit the truth in the simplest manner.... Saraswati would never hide or lie. She would say, 'You are doing your traditional job and we are doing ours. We don't know other jobs.' She would then pleasantly smile at the commenter.' Dhruv's entire novel, recently published in English, is a fascinating compendium of thug life that would rival the exploits of Tupac Shakur. Without sensationalism or nostalgia, Dhruv chronicles the everyday reality of living as a professional thief in the context of a criminalized society.[14]

The volume includes two personal testimonies towards the end, one from a descendant of the Ahmedabad settlement in Gujarat, and one from the infamous Solapur settlement in Maharashtra. Kalpana Gagdekhar's story is an extraordinary tale of success over a very short period of time. Hailing from a family of illegal bootleggers in Chharanagar, Kalpana (b. 1971?) has won acclaim in the field of Gujarati theatre. Indeed, in Mahatma Gandhi's birthplace, known for both official prohibition and unofficial bootlegging, someone born into a bootlegging community has portrayed the Mahatma's wife on the most visible stage of its largest city in the state's official language. Yet Kalpana comes from a tribal community speaking its own distinct dialect of Bantu, an Austro-Asiatic tribal language, in which this interview was conducted. Kalpana's interlocutor and translator, Roxy Gagdekhar (b. 1971?), is equally distinguished as a career journalist with the BBC Gujarati service reporting from Ahmedabad. He's assigned the crime beat without irony.

"Story of a hero who broke the fence..." by Bhimrao Jadhav (Guruji) (b. 1930) comes to us through the collection and translation by chair professor Chandrakant Puri (b. 1960), Rajiv Gandhi Centre for Contemporary Studies, University of Mumbai. Professor Puri began working with primitive tribal communities in Maharashtra in 1992, and since that time has initiated the PhD in Social Exclusion and Inclusive Policy Studies, the first of its kind in India. He continues field action and research with excluded communities such as tribal, dalit and nomadic and denotified tribes in Maharashtra. He is the recipient of several awards for his scholarship and activism. Of note is his work with prisoners of Ratnagiri special prison, which resulted in Mumbai University awarding him the Gold Medal in the year 1990.

Bhimrao Jadhav recounts the remarkable tale of ambient violence surrounding the criminal culture in the Solapur settlement, of which he was a long-time resident, and how village landlords would set criminal gangs against one another to settle old scores. Many died in such orchestrated mob violence. In the settlement itself, missionary conversion and malfeasance contributed to the insecurity of the inmates. Jadhav was instrumental in persuading the independent government of India to denotify the criminal tribes, and he personally witnessed the moment when the law minister came to Solapur to symbolically cut the fence, releasing the criminals into freedom. Jadhav comments: 'However, the bigger challenge remains, that is, when will the society remove their prejudices against us? My struggle continued.'

## Notes

1. Michel Foucault, *Discipline and Punish: The Birth of the Prison*, trans. Alan Sheridan (New York: Vintage, 1979).
2. There is now a growing literature on the history and sociology of crime in British India. See Anand Yang, ed., *Crime and Criminality in British India*, (Tucson: University of Arizona Press, 1985); Sandria Fritag, "Crime in the Social Order of Colonial North India," *Modern Asian Studies* 25.2 (1991): 227-61; Andrew Major, "State and Criminal Tribes in Colonial Punjab: Surveillance, Control and Reclamation of the 'Dangerous Classes'," *Modern Asian Studies* 33.3 (1999): 657-88; Radhika Singha, *A Despotism of Law: Crime and Justice in Early Colonial India* (New Delhi: Oxford University Press, 1998); Meena Radhakrishna, *Dishonoured by History: "Criminal Tribes" and British Colonial Policy* (New Delhi: Orient Longman, 2001); Mark Brown, "Ethnology and Colonial Administration in Nineteenth Century British India: The Question of Native Crime and Criminality," *British Journal of the History of Science* 36 (2003): 1-19; Clare Anderson, *Legible Bodies: Race, Criminality and Colonialism in South Asia* (Oxford: Berg, 2004); Henry Schwarz, *Constructing the Criminal Tribe in Colonial India* (Malden: Wiley-Blackwell, 2010).
3. Frederick Booth-Tucker, *Criminocurology, or the Indian Crim, and What to do with Him, Being a Review of the Work of the Salvation Army Among the Criminal Tribes of India*, 3rd. ed. (Simla: Royal Army Temperance Association, 1914).
4. Government of Bombay, *Annual Administrative Report on the Working of the Criminal Tribes Act in the Bombay Presidency* (Bombay: Government Printing House, 1924-46). Starte was the Backwards Class Officer for Bombay Presidency who signed the Reports.
5. Among the most important of these remains the Criminal Tribes Act Enquiry Committee of India, *Report of the Criminal Tribes Act Enquiry Committee, 1949–1950* (NP: 1950). The Committee's recommendations have not been implemented to date.

6. For an insider's perspective on the workings of the National Commission, see Marya Salim, "A National Commission that has Dismally Failed the Denotied Tribes" *The Wire*, 4 September 2018. https://www.academia.edu/36441938/A_National_Commission_That_Has_Dismally_Failed_the_Denotified_Tribes_The_Wire. Accessed 15 February 2020.
7. *Acting Like a Thief*. Dirs. Shaswati Talukdar and P. Kerim Friedman. DVD. Four Nine and a Half Productions, 2006.
8. For an overview of Budhan Theatre, see Schwarz (2010), chapter 4.
9. On the repetition and mimicry of 'historical sources,' see V.Y Mudinbe, *The Invention of Africa: Gnosis, Philosophy and the Order of Knowledge* (Bloomington: Indiana University Press, 1988); Mike Dash, *Thug: The True Story of India's Murderous Cult* (London: Granta, 2005); Joeanna Rebello, "Art of the 'Criminal Tribe'," *Times of India* 27/4/2008.
10. Booth-Tucker, *Criminocurology.*
11. Frederick Booth-Tucker, *Mukti Fauj, or Forty Years with the Salvation Army in India and Ceylon* (London: Marshall Brothers, Ltd., c. 1930); Radhakrishna.
12. O.H.B. Starte, *An Experiment in the Reformation of Criminal Tribes* (Bombay: Government Central Press, 1916); Starte, *Reformation of Offenders in India: A Handbook for the Use of Workers Amongst the Delinquents in India* (Bombay: Government Central Press, 1936).
13. Bernard S. Cohn, *Colonialism and its Forms of Knowledge: The British in India* (Princeton: Princeton University Press, 1996); Mike Davis, *Late Victorian Holocausts: El Nino Famines and the Making of the Third World* (New York: Verso, 2001).
14. Dhruv Bhatt, *The Pilgrims of Darkness*, trans. Vishal Bhadani. Preface by Henry Schwarz (Rajkot: Vedant Publications, 2019).

# 1

# Excerpt from *Budhan Bolta Hai*

Dakxin Bajrange

Autobiography and plays of Dakxin Bajrange, published by Bhasha Research and Publication Centre, Vadodara, 2010.
Translated by *Sonal*

*

I did not have a job and Maya, my wife, was growing concerned. All I did was theatre and social work which brought in no income. Things were dire. Out in Chharanagar the police were cracking down like never before and there was a severe shortage of foreign liquor and beer. If one could get ahold of them, they'd fetch very high prices. One day Maya declared, 'Come, let's go to Abu Road. If we travel together, nobody will suspect us. We can buy beer for cheap there. I will arrange for the mudi (seed money).'

I was hesitant. Our play, *Mujhe mat maro, saab*, was being staged and I was afraid that I would be arrested. Frustrated, Maya retorted, 'If you keep sitting idly, god is not going to come and give you money. One has to make an effort. The children have to listen to the taunts of their teachers every day. How long has it been since we last paid their fees? I can't bear it anymore. If you are not coming, I will go alone.'

Concerns about community, respect, propriety and Budhan Theatre crossed my mind. I was interrupted, 'You keep sitting here and thinking about it… I am going out to arrange for the mudi. Tomorrow, I will leave. I won't just sit here and do nothing.' Maya started to leave. I stopped her and said, 'Wait, I will come with you. Let us try this as well. Whatever fate wills.'

We left for Abu Road to purchase three boxes of alcohol. Maya had brought along plenty of wastepaper with her. She packed the boxes carefully, stuffing paper in between the bottles so they did not rattle. Carrying three boxes of beer left me sweating. With great difficulty we boarded a bus and waited anxiously till it crossed the check-post at the Rajasthan–Gujarat border. Only then did we heave a sigh of relief.

Maya had left Suhani, our small, still nursing daughter, at home. On the way back Maya's breasts, overflowing with milk, became stiff. She had not fed Suhani in two days and was writhing like a fish out of water. When the bus hit uneven, stony roads, Maya would cry out in pain. I did not know what to do. After a point she could not bear the pain anymore and she pressed her breasts to squeeze the milk out onto her palms. Tears streamed down her face. I was watching a mother's torment as she attempted to pay her children's school fees. She felt some relief only after she had squeezed some milk out. I had already called Rahul, a family member who was in the know about the underground business. He met us at Naroda–Patiya and had the boxes delivered in an auto rickshaw. We got some money and paid our children's fees.

With the passing of time, many things have changed. In their life of crime, and despite suffering severe repression and atrocities by the police, our grandparents' generation laid the foundations of education in our infamous community. Today, all children go to school. There is hundred per cent primary education in the community. The mother may brew liquor but she will make sure she sends her daughter to school. In Chharanagar, the distilleries start early in the morning. It is around the same time that young children leave for school. It has taken several generations of labour to create such a culture.

My pen is unsteady. My eyes are shrouded with sleep. Good night.

*

It was about six in the morning. Those were summer days when I slept on the terrace. Suddenly, I heard somebody wailing. When I peeped below to see what it was, I saw my aunt, Janna bhua, sitting on the roadside, beating her chest, wailing. Her daughter, Rina, sitting beside her, was singing mashiye, songs of mourning.

'Oh Munna, why did you leave us and go, why? We tried so many medicines, and still you left us.' Her son had passed away in the prime of his youth. Bhua's heart was torn in grief. 'My son … is this why I brought you up? Your mother is alone now. My dear boy, I told you, give up liquor, stop drinking … to hell with liquor, it snatched my son from me … for whom will I live now?'

I noticed that Jyoti, her second daughter-in-law, continued to brew liquor even as she handed a cup of tea to her child. It appeared as if everybody was expecting this day to arrive. Yes. Everyone knew. Munna had been confined to bed for the past several months. He was a heavy drinker and had been diagnosed with tuberculosis. Bhua would argue with him, try to reason with him, but he did not listen. Certain anxieties had been consuming him. With great difficulty, Bhua managed to get him off liquor but by that time the tuberculosis had become lethal.

Munna had not always been this way. He was once healthy and free of addiction. At his father's gambling den, he would operate card games like hajar, mangpatta and chakardi. He was a master at card games and earned a lot of money for his father. His winnings also brought us our meals and subsidized our education. I had hoped to someday pay him back all that I owed him. For the longest time, I would pass by him sprawled on his cot which stood on the street. A month before his death I suggested, 'Eh, Munna, you keep lying in bed all day. Why don't you go for a walk? Your body will gain some strength.'

'Oh, what can I do? I don't even have the energy to get up.'

'Are you still taking your medicines?'

'There is no money.'

'How about getting admitted in a government sanitorium

home? They will bear the expense of your treatment.'

'You help me. Here these bastards are bent on getting me killed.'

'Why?' I was taken aback.

'Don't you know the number of people who have purchased insurance policies in my name? When I die, all will become millionaires. Some six to seven of them have paid my premium,' Munna said despondently.

'You want to die so they can become millionaires? Tell me, what will you gain from all this?'

'Well, my wife will get ten per cent of the policy amount.'

'And how much is the policy amount?'

'Seven to eight lakh rupees.'

'Then your wife will get eighty thousand rupees. You think that is enough for her entire life? And what about the children?'

'The money will not last. I know that. But what can I do? People don't want me to get treatment. They are waiting for me to die. My wife has no money. Can I ask you something, Dakxin? Yaar, do whatever you can. I want to live.'

There were tears in his eyes—a lurking fear of death and a longing to live. I left him promising that I would get him admitted in a sanatorium.

That week I met with an accident. It was bad. After an operation, I was in bed for two months. In that time Munna passed away. I couldn't do anything. His cot was burnt along with his body. Bhua was free now. He was gone. Some heaved a sigh of relief, others lined up for their payouts.

Over the past decade, nearly two hundred individuals in our community have died an untimely death lured by insurance companies and the well-off and learned classes of the community. Those who have money enter into deals where they trade in the lives of young men—a social genocide. Young, both educated or otherwise, fall prey to their traps. Chharanagar's liquor consumes them. If there was even a single effort to oppose this, several of them would have been alive today. But their deaths were literal commodities far more valuable to the blood-sucking rich than their lives.

On paper, the wife or a family member are to be presented as nominee in order to receive the insurance amount, but through back-channel deals, insurance companies ensure that the amount goes directly to those paying the premium. Only then can the family visit the insurance company for their claim. The thumb impressions and signatures of the nominee are obtained in advance. Given the poverty, families are only too happy to receive even one-tenth of the total amount. That the rest of the money fills the coffers of the rich and powerful is not something that concerns them.

From the people of Chharanagar to the managers of insurance companies, everyone was part of this trade. Revealing these inner workings could cause trouble in my social life, but what I have narrated is true and I am prepared to face the consequences of owning up to it.

In the past, we Chharas were not this helpless. Outside the shadow of mainstream society, most members engaged in theft or brewing liquor. People were socially more organized. With an increase in education, urban culture gained ascendency. Its destructive ways were adopted wholesale by us. Had I not become a theatre artist or a writer, I would have turned out either as a bootlegger or a thief. Despite the lure of urban vices, perhaps it was the artist in me that kept temptation at bay. Through theatre, we have relived the lives of the people in our community. This expression gave us a new identity and transformed the artist within us. Living in a community held in disrepute, theatre allowed us to escape the hold of its debilitating limits and use our energies creatively.

As simple as it is now to sit here and write about this change, the process however was back-breaking. Because our plays were directly critical of the police and the establishment, the artists and their family members were often threatened with imprisonment. Actors also faced bitter resistance and hostility from their parents and spouses.

We performed every opportunity we got. Theatre developed a social commitment in us. A strength to fight injustice emerged. We became a voice for the nomadic and Denotified communities. Our voice reached every corner of the country. It made people look at us respectfully for once. Through the positive media attention we got, we hoped that a change in the outlook of lay people could be made.

I remember, I had once gone with some Adivasi artist friends to participate in the Gujarat Social Forum. One afternoon, we were having lunch at a restaurant. My friends had their traditional attire on. The rest of the city stared intently at them. Two elderly men were sitting opposite me. The tilak on their foreheads indicated their membership in the Swaminarayan sect. Their eyes too rested on my Adivasi companions.

Curiously, they asked me, 'Where have these people come from? They seem to be Adivasi.'

'They are Adivasi,' I said. 'They are from Chhota Udepur.'

Then they looked at me, 'Who are you? Where are you from?'

'My name is Dakxin. I live here, in Ahmedabad.'

'Where in Ahmedabad?'

'In Chharanagar,' I said as I continued eating.

'Chharanagar...,' they remarked, trying to recall something, 'I read somewhere that you do very good theatre.' Staring at me, one of them added, 'You people are no longer as you used to be. You have become artists.'

These words of recognition, from the educated class of society, felt like a dream to me. Our identity was beginning to be recognized as the 'voice against injustice'. But then again, on several occasions we were deeply humiliated for being Chharas.

Bhasha Centre and the Adivasi Academy had given me assignments to document nomadic and Denotified communities. I had gone to Tharad in the Banaskantha district of Gujarat with Vasant, a friend from the Bharwad community, and Lalji, who belonged to the Madari community. The Bharwads there had organized a huge fair. A ceremony was to take place at the temple of Lord Bholenath later. I had taken a small camera along. As part of the ceremony, a golden kalash was to be installed above the temple. I found a spot on the temple roof so I could shoot the event up close.

Suddenly, some people rushed in, sticks in hand, shouting and gesticulating for me to climb down. I had no idea what was happening. As soon as I was down, one of them pulled at my collar, another took hold of my trousers from behind, and two or three of them began hitting me. I was stunned, I failed to understand what was happening: they were trying to push me out. They placed the stick on my shoulders and trapped my hands in it. Meanwhile, Vasant and Lalji arrived. I was completely shaken. After the crowd had calmed down a bit, I asked, 'Bhai, what is the matter? Why are you beating me? What have I done?'

One of them retorted, 'What have you done? What were you doing there on top of the temple?'

'I was taking a photograph. What else?'

'Oh! Were you taking a photograph? Or were you planning on stealing the kalash?'

I felt as if someone had hit me on the head.

'Stealing the kalash? What are you talking about? I am not a thief. I am a filmmaker and I was taking photographs for the Adivasi Academy.'

This time someone struck my head for real.

'Give me your card. Which Adivasi Academy are you talking about? What Academy?'

'But I have not come here to steal...'

One of them cut me off, 'Shut up, you bastard. How dare you step inside our temple? Since the time you came here, I have had my eyes on you. Where do you stay? Tell us...,' so saying, he picked up his stick.

'Ahmedabad'.

'You are from Chharanagar, aren't you? A Chhara, aren't you? I know who you are. I have seen you. Get the hell out of here or we will break your limbs and hand you over to the police.'

I was scared; if the police arrived, the matter would get out of hand. Lalji and Vasant tried to reason with them but they would not listen. They kept pushing and shoving me. In fact, they sounded them off too, 'You should be ashamed, making friends with the Chharas.'

Turning to Lalji, they asked, 'Who is he?' Lalji looked afraid.

Vasant replied, 'He is with us, his name is Lalji.'

'Which caste is he?'

'He is a Madari. But...'

Cutting Vasant short, one of them said, 'Get him going as well.'

They shoved us outside the temple premises. Vasant and Lalji were mortified. I went outside and stood in a corner, waiting for the kalash to be installed so I could take a picture. When I was done, I returned home. Whenever such incidents occur, I try not to get dejected. In fact, I feel more inspired to carry on with my struggle. Perhaps because such experiences have become a common part of our lives.

Several times in my life, I have depended entirely on the support of others. I always wanted to become a film director. This imaginative urge also helped me to write and direct plays. While I practiced theatre in Chharanagar, I also travelled extensively for my films. My friend, Nainesh, helped me a lot in this struggle. Whenever I needed money, Nainesh would give me some hundred rupees with which I would refill my scooter and start out. Sometimes Nainesh would help me out, on other occasions Sunil, and then also my parents, dadi or bhua. I never felt ashamed asking for money. It was being used for important work.

Meanwhile, I found work with Bhasha Centre and was given the responsibility of training students of the Adivasi Academy in Tejgadh, in theatre and film production. These classes were held three days a week. So I divided my time working between Chharanagar and Tejgadh, three days in each place, as I was still working with my theatre troupe. I was spared only a day to spend with my children. Much of whatever I managed to earn after running around so much would go towards my brother Uttar's education. The financial situation at home was very bad.

One day I had gone to the Bhasha Centre's office for a meeting with G.N. Devy. Also present at the meeting were some people from the Madari community in Kothamba—Babunath and Arjunath Madari. Mahasweta Devi was also in Baroda at that time. After the pleasantries, Dr Devy showed us a Gujarati news clipping that carried a report on the inhuman atrocities being perpetrated on the Madaris by the forest department and the Animal Help Foundation. He read it out loud, and then turning to me he asked if I could make a five-minute film about the issue.

I was always ready to make films and plays, so I agreed immediately. As I was shooting I tried to get to the root of the Madaris' problem. So it was that I decided to make the Madari community act in the film. It was to be a real performance derived from experience. It was based on a real-life incident—an animal rights' NGO had the snake-charming Madari community arrested, and the people had been locked up in dog cages. They were left without a livelihood. After I finished it, *Fight for Survival* was screened at various fora. There was much discussion on the atrocities being perpetrated by animal rights organizations and the forest department. It was the beginning of a dialogue on the subject, and I gained much recognition through it. In 2005, the film won the second prize at the Jeevika: Asia Livelihood Documentary Festival that showcases documentaries based on the issue of livelihood.

The award included a handsome trophy and twenty-five-thousand rupees as prize money. More than the award I was happy to receive the money: my younger sister Chetna was to get married in a few months. The wedding date had been decided, but we were finding it difficult to arrange for the expenses. My elder sisters, Neelam, Kunta, Koina, were all trying their best. So, when I received twenty-five-thousand rupees it felt as if I had won the world.

The award money came to me through a cheque. I made several visits to the bank to encash it. Expecting to receive it soon, we had taken out a loan for Chetna's wedding. But the money never got deposited thanks to some bureaucratic muddle. Meanwhile the lenders were adding to the pressure.

Come 2006, I was away attending to the theatre training of my Adivasi friends at Tejgadh. There I learnt that my daughter Suhani had fallen ill. The doctor informed me that she had a blood deficiency and that I'd have to arrange for a blood donation. Suhani had to be admitted. The police had by now consented to let us run our gambling business, so some money was arranged from there. My wife, Maya, was seven months pregnant and she too was running low on blood. The doctor informed me, 'If she is not given blood immediately there may be complications in the delivery.' Somehow I had been able to arrange money for Suhani's hospitalization, but now I had to do the same for Maya too. I had to borrow money again. Life goes like this for us. It seems like we keep running from one crisis to another. Putting out fires even as we forget to breathe.

In March the same year, a nomadic and Denotified communities fair was held at Kaleshwari where we performed three plays: *Mujhe mat maro, saab* [Don't beat me, Sir], *Idgaah* [Prayer ground] and *Ulgulan* [The Great Tumult]. By 2003, the Indian government had formed a National Commission for Denotified, Nomadic and Semi-Nomadic Tribes, and Mr Laxmi Chand, member secretary of the commission, came to visit the fair. After discussing the issues of the Bhantu community we invited him to watch our plays.

We were to perform in the scorching heat outdoors. It felt as if the ground itself was on fire. Standing there without footwear was next to impossible. Yet, all of us performed barefoot. By the end, we all had sores on our feet. In our passion to narrate our stories, we completely forgot about the blistering heat. None of the actors complained. Even the child actors of Chharanagar performed on the burning surface for a couple of minutes. I had tears in my eyes. From beyond the stage one could tell that it was painful. but the actors gave a superb performance. Jeetu was the lead actor of *Mujhe mat maro, saab.* His father had been in prison for six months and his bail application had been rejected twice by the high court. Back in the day, both our fathers were partners in crime, quite literally thick as thieves. And now we were here together. On the day of the performance the bail application was being filed for the third time. We were all hoping for the best. But the plea was rejected once again.

Jeetu was shattered. At first he refused to perform. But being a firm practitioner of the adage, 'The show must go on', he took the stage anyway.

Sandeep, another of our fellow troupe members, who had been in prison for the past three months on false charges of homicide, was out on parole for eighteen days so he could write his university exams. He had to return to prison on 28 March 2006. The performance was on 26 March. Sandeep came to me a day before the performance and said, 'Dakxin... I want to perform before I go back to prison. Please take me to Kaleshwari.' I could see how passionate he was. I did not even ask him to rehearse. I was confident he would be able to improvise during the performance. Like a bird, Sandeep was always ready to take wing, and perhaps it was theatre that helped him survive the cage-like walls of the prison. Sandeep had a bit of a stammer, but surprisingly, even without any rehearsal, he gave an excellent performance at Kaleshwari.

*

Earlier that month, on 2 March, the Ahmedabad Municipal Corporation had once again demolished the Maninagar settlement. All the residents were left homeless. At the time I had gone with Vinod Raja, the acclaimed filmmaker of *The Bee, The Bear and The Kuruba*, to a village called Bhat for a preliminary visit—we were making a documentary on the local dancer-community called Raj Nats. When we heard the news, we rushed to Maninagar immediately. Children were crying, women were hurling abuses. Older people were gathering their broken belongings. The corporation authorities had confiscated even the cot of a hundred-and-twenty-five-year-old woman. The women of Maninagar had been brutally beaten up by the police. Amidst the rubble, two small children were laughing as they looked at what was happening with their tiny eyes. One was four-days-old, the other had completed nine days. Their mothers were crouching under the shade of a nearby tree with their children.

The government and the residents who lived in nearby neighbourhoods were bent on forcing the Maninagar communities into becoming nomadic again. They had been living in Maninagar since 1960. But they were always assumed to be thieves, even though they worked extremely hard to earn their livelihoods.

I was angry. It was time to go on a hunger strike. If we sit back silently, the government will be only too happy to drive us away and kill us off. In any case, people were already dying of hunger. Out of fear of the authorities, nobody wanted to risk going out for work. As if this was not enough, the police were now constantly patrolling the area. All the people who had been made homeless and destitute were roundly beaten up whenever they were spotted settling down on the streets. People had to become vigilant, they'd hurriedly gather their things and stumble away as soon as there was a hint of police presence. If anybody protested they were brutally lathi-charged with no concern for age or gender. A sense of terror had spread through the community.

Meanwhile, Vijay ranked first in the state examination held for selection of police constables. He had been working with the Budhan Theatre for a long time, and he was also involved with the Chharanagar Library and other education projects in the locality. His only dream was to become a police officer. Now it had come true.

My dear friend, Roxy, was in Gandhinagar to discuss the Maninagar issue with G.N. Devy. I am not privy to the details of the discussion but I received a call from Roxy saying, 'Dr Devy is saying that we should hold a hunger strike on the Maninagar issue day after tomorrow. We need to bring together a hundred people.' Because I was all set to conduct a theatre workshop in Tejgadh, Dr Devy told me to go ahead with it. In the meantime, Roxy began preparations for the hunger strike.

The day was 23 March 2006. I was noting down the date for some reason and I remembered that Bhagat Singh, Sukhdev and Rajguru were hanged on this very day in 1931. The revolutionary poet Pash too had been killed on this day back in 1988. I remember a poem by Pash.

Those who have sung the songs of swords
Their words are formed with blood
Blood is made of iron
Those who live on the borders of death
Their deaths begin the journey of life
Those whose blood and sweat mix in the soil
They rise from the soil.

I picked up my phone. Since I had not paid my bill yet, outgoing calls were barred. But I could still send text messages. I typed the poem out and sent it to my friends. The people of this country have forgotten Bhagat Singh's sacrifice. We have forgotten his ideology, his fight, his message of martyrdom, everything. When Bhagat Singh,

Sukhdev and Rajguru went willingly to their deaths, they probably did not have the India we have created in mind. Perhaps the India of their dreams died along with them. I feel if we gain inspiration from Bhagat Singh's love for books, half of the country's problems would be solved.

Pash was murdered because he wrote about the Khalistani movement and expressed his views against the government. In my experience, I have learnt that the state silences people in two ways. First, it tries to buy them off and give up on the ideals they hold. And if that doesn't work, it sentences them to death.

About a hundred and fifty people joined Dr Devy in the hunger strike. At that time I was on my way to Tejgadh. I sent word out to all my friends to support the strike in whatever way it was possible, be it direct or indirect participation. Some three hundred people responded. The hunger strike sent a strong message of opposition to the government. Many other organizations had also joined us. The very same day at three in the afternoon, the municipal commissioner, Anil Mukim, came with his officers to discuss the issue with us and promised to give land to a hundred and two families. This was a huge victory for us. We heaved a huge sigh of relief in our jubilation.

People of all ages and genders participated in the protest. Two recent mothers joined in with their infants, despite the intense heat. Both the women had not eaten anything since morning, their breasts had no milk, making their children unwitting participants in the hunger strike.

As of today, the situation of the nomadic and Denotified tribes hasn't improved much. To obtain a ten-by-ten-foot piece of land, one has to visit the corporation office some two hundred times. Some people do this for years together. Even then the corporation rarely takes any action. When the judiciary gives its approval to 'remove the poor', others take it as an excuse to hound them for their blood. When the people of the Maninagar settlement went to reclaim their possessions at the municipal office, they got nothing back. This despite the deputy commissioner J.D. Saya's promise to return them their belongings. In the unfolding of this process, the officers of the municipal corporation showed us their true colours and where their loyalties lay. We were tired. Mukesh, a friend from Maninagar, came up to me and said, 'In the last two days we have spent about five hundred rupees on travel alone. We no longer have the strength to fight.' His voice betrayed how little faith he had left in the government. He told me that many children had become unwell because of the heat. I felt like we had all fallen ill.

# 2

# Bulldozer

Dakxin Bajrange

Translated by *Sonal*

## Playwright's Notes

One day while I was at the Bhasha Research Centre attending a meeting, I met a Pappu Sansi from Vadodara. He told me about the plight of the Sansis of Ahmedabad. After living a nomadic life for years, the Sansi community from Rajasthan had come to live here in the city. They gave themselves a new name, 'Dabgar'.

Residing near the Maninagar railway crossing, these poor families had their dwellings demolished multiple times by the Ahmedabad Municipal Corporation. Although they had been living there for the past several years, these nomadic families had suddenly become a blot on the beauty of the city. They had been asked to submit documents of land ownership, which they obviously did not have. A five-year-long wait for a decision, sixty-five visits to the Ahmedabad Municipal Corporation, several petitions, a hunger strike—all possible efforts were made. Their struggle for a piece of ten-by-ten-foot land continues; they continue to retain their faith in the Supreme Court of India.

These nomads, who earn their livelihood by selling printed maps on street corners, simply wish to settle down. But the government has no address to give them. *Bulldozer* is inspired by the lived experiences, the despair and hope, the incidents which informed the lives of this community.

## Characters

ACTORS 1–8
INSANE MAN/JUDGE
POLICE CONSTABLE
POLICE STATION IN-CHARGE
MUKESH
RAKHI
MUNNA
RAJU
RAMYA
PAKYA
CHHOTU
OLD MAN
MAUSI
GAURI
RAJESH
KALLU
MANGA
RAMSARUP
MONTY
MANJU
MALA
OLD WOMAN
RESHAMIYA
OFFICER 1
OFFICER 2
POLICE INSPECTOR
MAYURBHAI
MUNICIPAL CORPORATION WORKER
WOMAN
BASTIWALA (COMMUNITY RESIDENT)
SEEMA
CHILD 1
CHILD 2

## Scene One

(*All the actors are sitting in the audience. Drum beats begin. Suddenly, a voice calls from within the audience.*)

ACTOR 1: Friends… Come, let us begin the play…

(*Drum beats.*)

ACTOR 2: This is a play within a play, O friend,

A play within a play…

ALL: A play in the form of a play, my friend

A play as play…

This is a play for the oppressed, O friend

A play about survival

Of the labourers

Of the hungry,

A play as play,

For the survival

Of workers and

Of the hungry

A play played as a play, O friend…

A play as a play,

The system is a mirror

The system is a mirror…

This is the silence of death… silence…

This is the silence of death… silence…

Children are crying….

Bodies are hanging in our homes…

A play being played as a play, O friend…

Cut the forests

Divide the land

Sell the rivers

Cut the forests, divide the land, sell the rivers

Cut the forests, divide the land, sell the rivers
Sell...sell...sell...
O brothers... sell even our country
Sell the country... sell even the country
We play this play
In the streets, the community, village and city
We perform this play
We raise our voice, we protest
We present the truth
With this play of the poor
A play as a play, O friend...
A play as play....

(*After the song, actors 4,5,6,7 and 8 come and sit centre stage. Actors 1, 2 and 3 assume the role of police constables, walk on to the stage and encircle them.*)

ACTORS 1, 2, 3: Who are you?

ACTORS 4, 5, 6, 7, 8: We are nomads, sir.

ACTORS 1, 2, 3: Where have you come from?

ACTORS 4, 5, 6, 7, 8: We are nomads, sir.

ACTORS 1, 2, 3: Where will you go?

ACTORS 4, 5, 6, 7, 8: We are nomads, sir.

ACTORS 1, 2, 3: For how long have you been here?

ACTORS 4, 5, 6, 7, 8: Longer than you, sir.

ACTORS 1, 2, 3: Mind your tongue...

ACTORS 4, 5, 6, 7, 8: We will watch our words, sir... we will watch our words...

ACTORS 1, 2, 3: What work do you do?

ACTOR 4: Traditionally, we are artists. But we have lost our forests and land, so now we beg for our survival.

ACTORS 1, 2, 3: Artists? We know what kind of artists you are.

We have been taught that all you tribals are 'born criminals'.

(*The nomads look scared.*)

ACTOR 5: No, sir. We are not thieves… we are not thieves…. We practice our traditional arts for our livelihood. We work as daily wage labourers… as farm labourers… as craftsmen…. We are not thieves.

ACTORS 1, 2 AND 3: Stop rambling and come to the police station with us.

ALL: Police station?

(*Sound of drum beats.*)

## Scene Two

(*All actors take their positions for the next scene.*)

CHORUS: How wonderful is this pen!

When it writes, it has the power to change destinies
To change fortunes.
It becomes voice for some,
A prison for others.
The pen is a sword, a pistol,
Like life, it has many colours.
Its ink
Is the past, present and future.
One day
Just two drops of its red ink caused
Children to die
Homes to be destroyed
Families to become homeless
The poor to become wanderers
Their insides cried out in hunger,
'Do not destroy my home, brother!'

An alien idea
Was imported:
'Clean the city!
Here, there, everywhere.
Make it beautiful, beautiful, beautiful!'
How can this happen?
This is a democracy, my brother.
Anything is possible here.
For the government controls the pen and the ink, my brother.
Here, there, everywhere
Make it beautiful… beautiful… beautiful...

(*An actor speaks as the* JUDGE *and acts as an intelligent but insane person.*)

INSANE MAN: Stop this shouting.

(*Feeling frightened, everybody disperses.*): Oh! Look, the madman has come, the madman is here.

INSANE MAN: How dare you call me mad? It is those who call the mad 'mad' that are mad.

ALL: Forgive us, we are sorry.

JUDGE: Okay, I pardon you. Nothing will be achieved this way. You will have to work. My pen gives you the power. You are government servants. You are all bureaucrats. Therefore, there should be no emotions, no sentiments, only implementation of orders. We have to make this country beautiful. So, the poor of this country… I mean, Here, there, everywhere…
Make everything beautiful…beautiful…beautiful…

ACTOR 5: Now this mad man is talking sense.

ACTOR 6: Why should he not? He is a mad man in power.

ALL: Power?

(*Drum beats.*)

## Scene Three

ACTOR 1: There is good news... news for us to rejoice.

ALL: Good news?

ACTOR 1: Yes, there's good news for all police stations in the city.

ALL: News for the police stations?

ACTOR 2: Here are the highlights from today's newspapers.

ACTOR 3: *Sandesh* newspaper.

ACTOR 4: The police has caught a Chhara gang for looting.

ACTOR 5: *Gujarat Samachar.*

ACTOR 6: Two dangerous Dafers were killed in an encounter.

ACTOR 7: *The Times of India.*

ACTOR 8: Two Pardhis were arrested for multiple robberies and thefts.

ACTOR 1: This is the City police station.

POLICE CONSTABLE: Sir, what do we do with these Sansis?

POLICE STATION IN CHARGE: Oh, you dumb donkey! Who appointed you as constable? File an FIR against them.

POLICE CONSTABLE: Okay, sir. But on what charges?

POLICE STATION IN CHARGE: (*Angrily*) Where were you trained? What but the IPC 394 and 395 which were especially created for the Pardhis.

POLICE CONSTABLE: Okay, sir.

POLICE STATION IN CHARGE: And listen. Inform all police stations in the city by wireless about the arrest of these Sansi nomads. It will bring relief to many.

(*Drum beats.*)

## Scene Four

*(It is afternoon. One can see the slums in the centre of the city. The slum comprises several small and big shanties put up with sheets of torn plastic and old, worn out clothes. People are moving about, children are playing with pebbles. Somebody is cleaning vessels, others are engaged in a quarrel.* MUKESH *is sitting in his shanty, having his food. His wife is cooking. A heap of neem twigs is lying outside* MUKESH*'s house.)*

MUKESH: It is cold today. Don't go out to beg.

RAKHI: (*Preparing chappatis*) What will we eat at night if I do not go out to beg? Munni seems to have chicken pox. Bhagat was saying that goddess Mataji has possessed her and manifested as chicken pox on her body. (*Looking at* MUNNI) The poxes on her body are increasing. She had high fever last night. I tied some neem leaves together in the morning as an offering to Mataji. Please, do not forget to take it to the temple in the evening.

MUKESH: Okay. (*Finishes his food and washes his hands.*)

RAKHI: What happened at the police station yesterday?

MUKESH: What do you think? That bastard Patel thrashed everybody. It was good that the headman was present. It was only when he finally called a lawyer that we were released. Otherwise we would have faced a long stint in jail.

RAKHI: These bastards don't leave us in peace in our own neighbourhood, forget anywhere else. This morning the police had come again. They were saying that they are bringing a bulldozer to raze our settlement.

MUKESH: (*Alarmed*) What are you saying? (*Wondering*) When did he say?

RAKHI: He said they will arrive at ten in the morning. (*Frightened*) Do you think they will really come with the bulldozer? Where will we take Munni?

MUKESH: Where is Raju?

(*Drum beats.*)

### Scene Five

(*It is the other end of the settlement. A group of five to six men are sitting in a circle, playing a gambling game called dana. This game is commonly played in community ghettos. The players sit in a circle and throw two dice. The judgment is called 'tiri'. If both the dice show a single dot (pon) or three dots (tiri), the person who tossed the dice is declared to have lost the game. If the dice bear four (chaunk) or six (chakka) dots, the player wins the game. Generally, the players shout in excitement and throw around terms related to the game, such as 'Baba ki do ankhiya' (two dots on the dice), 'Chuut tiri' (three on the dice), 'Bam bam bole' (six on the dice), 'Aati... aati...', 'Come... come....', for tiri and pon and 'Bara ka bara' (twelve dots), 'Das aur do, bara' (ten and two make four), 'Aati chaunk' (here comes four) and so on for chakka and chaunk.*)

RAJU: (*Tosses the dice in his hand. Places a ten-rupee note.*) Look, how this disappears... poof! Is there anyone who dares to play a ten-rupee game... Poof!

RAMYA: It is two poofs, brother... It is two poofs... This is ten rupees. Come on, throw a tiri.

RAJU: (*Tossing the dice in his hands, places a ten-rupee note*) Okay, okay. This has also gone poof... poof... poof... Is there a man here?

PAKYA: It's two poofs, brother. Okay, now throw two ankhiya.

Men feel no pain.

RAJU: (*Smiling*) It's coming, my dear friends. Here come your two ankhiya and your tiri... (*Tosses the dice*) See! How your father brings twelve ankhiya. (*Throws the die and shouts*) Throw a six.

PAKYA: (*Follows the movement of the dice on the ground and shouts*) Tiri, tiri!

RAMYA: Ankhiya, ankhiya!

(*The judgment stops at 'tiri' and* RAJU *loses the game.* RAMYA *happily picks up the ten rupee note.*)

RAJU: Get lost! What luck today... Wonder whose face I woke up and saw today.

PAKYA: Hey, Raju. Hand over the ten rupees.

RAJU: Hey, I will give you a tenner. I am not a beggar like you. (*Takes out a ten rupee note from his pocket*) Here, take this. Come now, it's your turn. Throw the dice. (*The dice is in* RAMYA*'s hands.*)

RAJU: (*Bets twenty rupees*) Okay. Poof! Ramya... loses, Ramya loses! Ramya, it's a gul...

CHHOTU: Two gul. Come Ramya, throw twelve ankhiya.

RAJU: Hey, tilli ki tiri is coming!

RAMYA: (*Betting ten rupees*) Oh, come on! I bet again.

(*An* OLD MAN *is sitting in a nearby tea stall*)

OLD MAN: Hey, Raju. Come throw the dice. I have a feeling that you will win. Come on accept Ramya's challenge. You will win.

RAJU: (*Happily*) Really... What are you saying, man? If I win this game then these ten rupees are yours. Hey, Ramya, here goes your money... Come on Ramya, now throw Baba ki do ankhiya.

RAMYA: (*Twirling the dice in his hands*) Not Baba ki do ankhiya. Here come twelve ankhiya. (*He throws the dice. Everyone shouts*) Look!

RAMYA: (*Shouting*) Chhut chhakka!

PAKYA: Chhut chonk.

RAJU: Baba ki do ankhiyan…

(*No judgement is taken.* RAJU *throws the dice. The players and the viewers, all shout aloud*)

RAJU: Oh, let it be a six.

PAKYA: Do ankhiyan.

RAMYA: Throw a tiri.

(RAJU *throws a tiri. He throws the die forcefully.*)

PAKYA AND RAMYA: No one will touch the money. It is all ours!

(RAJU, *who has lost the game, spots the* OLD MAN *as he tries to sneak away.*)

RAJU: Hey, old man. Where are you running off to? Bastard, you have a false tongue.

OLD MAN: What can I do if your luck is bad? Here, have some tea.

RAJU: (*Getting furious*) You're a bad omen. To hell with your tea! Go away, or I will hang you upside down and thrash you. Get lost!

(MUKESH *comes running in.*)

RAJU: What happened? Is a dog chasing you?

MUKESH: Not one dog. Many!

RAJU: Stop your nonsense. I lost a lot of money today. (*Lights a bidi*) Tell me, what's the matter? (*The others continue their game.*)

MUKESH: Don't waste your money. Save it to rebuild your

shack.

RAJU: What is this nonsense now?

MUKESH: Tomorrow the corporation authorities are coming to bulldoze our entire settlement.

(*Everyone sitting around the tea stall stands up*)

RAJU: What are you saying? Today is a bad... unfortunate day... unlucky...

PAKYA: If they come and demolish our shacks, where will we go in this cold winter?

RAJU: (*Angrily*) Those bastards... Even last year these bastards had demolished our homes in winter. My...my...three-year-old Tiniya died in the biting cold... he froze to death... Who knows whose turn is next?

RAMYA: And that old uncle, Manikaka! He went to sleep in the open at night and never woke up.

MUKESH: (*Worried*) My baby is down with chicken pox.

RAJU: My sister-in-law is due for delivery any time now...

CHHOTU: Raju, we need to do something. Or we will be ruined in this cold!

RAJU: What can we do? In the last ten years our settlement has been demolished nine times. And we could do nothing.

MAUSI: Earlier they used to send us an advance notice of ten to fifteen days. We got some time to move our belongings. Now these bastards come whenever they feel like.

ALL: Bulldozer... brother... bulldozer... corporation bulldozer...

**Scene Six**

*(It is eight in the night. The stoves are burning in some of the settlement's shanties. There is a strong wind blowing. A five-year-*

*old child is crying in one of the plastic shacks.* GAURI, *the child's mother, is grinding chutney. There is a hubbub in the settlement as people come and go.)*

GAURI: (*Shouting angrily at the child*) Oh, why are you tearing your vocal cords so? Has your father died or what? The bastard must be lying drunk somewhere. God knows whose ears he is cleaning at this time of the night. Be quiet! Or I will give you a sound thrashing... What do you want?

CHILD: (*Crying*) Give me a chapati. I am hungry.

GAURI: I'll give it to you, but wait a while. What a strong wind is blowing. Let the breeze abate so that I can put on the fire and cook something for you.

(GAURI*'s husband,* RAJESH, *walks in.*)

RAJESH: (*Sitting down in the shack which is quivering in the wind*) What is the matter? Why are you crying?

GAURI: Why are you so late? Do people want to get their ears cleaned this late in the night?

RAJESH: Oh, I returned at about six. Ramsarup uncle started discussing village matters with me, so I got delayed. (*The child is still crying.* RAJESH *shouts at his son*) Stop your wailing! What do you want?

GAURI: He is asking for chapattis. I told him to wait a while till the wind dies down. But he just doesn't listen.

RAJESH: Oh, so prepare a chapatti. The wind will not stop. (*Explaining*) It's winter now. He is bound to feel hungrier.

GAURI: What's it to me? I will cook in the wind. You can both eat your food with dust in it.

RAJESH: Yes, yes. We'll eat. You prepare chapattis for us quickly. (*Calling out to his son*) Kallu, come here. (KALLU *goes to his father. He is still crying.*) Oh, be quiet. Look, I scolded your mother, so stop crying now. Sing for me the song you were singing yesterday. What was that song… The one in the play that this group came to perform yesterday… what was the name of the play? Yes… *Bulldozer…*

(KALLU *starts singing.*)

KALLU: Bulldozla… bhai Bulldozla… colpolation... Bulldozla.

RAJESH: Oh, wonderful... You remember the song.

(GAURI *is preparing chapattis. The wind is blowing strong. The plastic sheet is flapping away.*)

GAURI: Raju. What did Ramsarup uncle say? After you left for work in the morning, some policemen from Rambaug came over. They told us to pack our belongings and leave. Apparently, people from the municipal corporation will be here tomorrow morning to demolish everything…

MANGA: (*A thin man whose face is swollen with liquor is sitting in a corner, drinking and shouting*) How can they demolish our homes s-s-sons of bitches… Tomorrow, I will lie down in front of their bulldozer. Let's see how they break our homes.

RAJESH: Oh, Manga…if they wish they can erase us along with our houses under their bulldozer… Now the government speaks of removing the poor, not poverty.

MANGA: You are absolutely right. They want to kill people like us. They will build a mega city over our dead bodies.

RAJESH: (*As* GAURI *serves him*) We have been wandering since childhood. It is with so much difficulty that we finally found shelter here. Now this too will be taken away from us. I don't know… Where do I take my children in this cold winter?

MANGA: Don't go anywhere. We'll not survive if we leave this place.

(MUKESH *walks in.*)

MUKESH: Rajesh, Manga, come, hurry up. Ramsarup uncle has called a meeting. Everybody is gathering at the tea stall. Come quickly. (MUKESH *leaves.*)

MANGA: One more meeting? What is the use? We cannot fight the government in silence. We should all lay ourselves down before the bulldozer. Only then will we be able to save our home. There is nobody higher and more powerful than the government!

**Scene Seven**

(*It is night. A cold wind is blowing. A few children, some old people and young men have gathered at the tea stall on the edge of the settlement. The entire slum is visible from this point. There are no lights here. There is a single street light set up by the municipal corporation which burns and flickers out as it pleases. The meeting is conducted in the brightness of the lanterns.*)

RAMSARUP: Oh brothers, the government is so big. How can pebbles like us resist them?

MANGA: You mean that we should vacate?

RAMSARUP: I did not say that. What is to be done? I have called this meeting to discuss this.

MANGA: What is to be done? These bastards have demolished our settlement ten times in the last eight years. Tomorrow they will do it again. If we are to stop them, then all of us should lie down before their bulldozer.

RAMYA: And what if they run the bulldozer over us?

MANGA: Then what? We'll die. What else?

RAMYA: Great! Such brave talk, Manga. Show your bravery after you get over your hangover tomorrow morning.

MANGA: (*Angrily*) I am not a coward like you. If you have the guts, then you too come here tomorrow morning.

RAMYA: Oh, yes! We'll all see how you will be quietly standing there.

MANGA: Watch your words, Ramya. Or else...

RAMSARUP: Listen, my brothers. This is not the time to quarrel. This is the moment to reflect, to find a way out of this difficulty.

(RAMYA *and* MANGA *become quiet.*)

MUKESH: (*To the tea stall owner*) Hey, Tony. Serve us all your special strong tea. We all need to calm down.

MANGA: Mukya, get a drink for me.

MUKESH: Be quiet now. Let me speak.

RAMYA: I have an idea. Why not place our children in front of the bulldozer? Surely, they will not run the bulldozer over children!

PAKYA: Did you read the newspaper yesterday? The Mumbai corporation was demolishing slums in their city and in one of them they crushed a small girl sitting inside. These people have no heart. We cannot risk putting our children before their bulldozer!

CHACHA: Then what do we do? If we do not pack our meagre belongings and move elsewhere by tonight, then they will take everything away in the morning. That would mean death for us in these cold, wintry nights.

RAMSARUP: Mukesh, can the petitions you have given to the corporation not help in any way?

MUKESH: What more can happen, uncle? We have already submitted more than sixteen petitions, requesting that we be provided with an alternate site for living. But not once have they replied to us. It has been two and a half years since we started making rounds of the corporation office.

(TONY *serves tea.*)

RAMSARUP: Look, brothers. In the past few days we even met Mukim sir, the commissioner. He promised to give houses to nomadic communities.

RAMYA: Oh! Don't pay heed to these government promises, uncle. The government and the government servants! They are all alike.

(*Suddenly a woman rushes in.*)

MANJU: Hey, Rakesh, Rakesh…

RAKESH: (*Getting up*) What's the matter, Manju? Where are you running off to?

MANJU: Hurry up and come. Ganga has trouble breathing. She is running a high temperature. (*She begins to cry.*) She is gasping like a fish. Come, come quickly. Your wife is calling you.

(*Everyone gets up hurriedly.*)

RAKESH: (*With tears in his eyes*) Uncle, forgive me. This is a serious matter and I do wish to stay on, but Ganga…

RAMSARUP: What nonsense are you talking? You go... Rush home and take your wife to the hospital.

(RAKESH *leaves with* MANJU.)

MUKESH: Poor Rakesh. He spends the whole day cleaning

people's ears, and half of whatever little he earns is spent on his child. It's like the hole in Ganga's heart has made a hole in Rakesh's life as well.

RAMSARUP: (*To* MONTY) Monty, please go and help Rakesh. Go, run!

(MONTY *exits.*)

MUKESH: (*Quivering*) Uncle… my daughter has chicken pox… Goddess Mataji has possessed her and her whole body is infected. She cannot sleep because of the pain.

RAMYA: My wife is eight months pregnant now. Where should I take her?

PAKYA: My child is barely a month old. Where can I go to provide him a roof?

MALA: And where do I take my hundred-and-five-year-old mother? Brother Ramsarup, we need to do something, or I'll lose my mother along with our hut.

RAMSARUP: Don't talk like that, sister Mala. Let us hope that god averts such a calamity. Your mother will live till she is a hundred and fifteen.

MALA: I hope that goddess Jogmaya makes yours words come true. After my husband passed away, my mother is the only family I have. (*Almost crying.*) I have made a pledge to goddess Jogmaya. If our settlement is not demolished tomorrow, I will offer her a coconut.

MUKESH: (*To* RAMSARUP) Uncle! Why don't we meet the corporator of our locality? He may be able to help us.

PAKYA: Who? That Mayurbhai? Aye, what will that fascist do?

RAMSARUP: (*Angrily*) What is the harm in meeting him? Whomsoever he supports or believes in, he is the corporator of our locality after all. He holds power in this municipality. The municipality will at least listen to him, if not us.

PAKYA: Uncle, you don't know. A few days back, when my son, Tiniya, went to the other side of Ahmedabad to sell maps, the Children's Home people took him away assuming he was a beggar.

RAMSARUP: Then?

PAKYA: When I went to have Tiniya released, that bastard of a superintendent asked me to obtain a letter from the local corporator as evidence that I have been living in Ahmedabad for all these decades. And further, to produce my ration card as proof that Tiniya is my child.

RAMYA: What did you do then?

PAKYA: What could I have done? I rushed to Mayurbhai and narrated what had happened. Do you know what he said?

MUKESH: What?

PAKYA: (*Mimicking* MAYURBHAI) He asked, 'Where do you live?' I said, 'Here. In the Dabgarvas settlement behind the railway station.' He immediately retorted, 'I have never seen you there.' I lost my temper, I too shot back. I said, 'Sir, I think you have forgotten. You came to my house.' He said, 'What? I came to your house? When?' I replied, 'At the time of elections. To ask for votes.' (*All laugh aloud.*)

RAMYA: (*Surprised*) What are you saying? You said that to him? What happened then?

PAKYA: What would happen? He was enraged. He said, 'I am going to count the votes of your entire settlement. I'll check whom you have all voted for.'

MUKESH: What happened to your Tiniya?

PAKYA: He rotted in the Children's Home for two whole days. I managed to get him out only after greasing the superintendent's beak.

MUKESH: Uncle, if Mayurbhai is such a man, then there is no use going to him.

RAMSARUP: (*Worried*) So what do we do now? I cannot think of anything.

OLD WOMAN: (*Walking with the help of a stick.*) Ramsarup, son, the poor never live in the past or the future. We have to live in the present to stay alive. (*She stops to look at everybody.*) If poor people like us are alive today it is because of god's grace, otherwise this government and these money lenders... It is too late in the night now. Fight tomorrow's battles tomorrow. Go, go back to your homes. Get some sleep.

## Scene Eight

(*It's a dark, wintery night. The municipality's street light is flickering, brightening the settlement one moment and blackening it the next. It is midnight, but the settlement-dwellers are unable to sleep. Some people are packing their belongings, others are putting their vessels in place. A few children have lit a fire outside to keep themselves warm. One can hear the laughter of children. Close by, a drunkard is rambling aloud. Suddenly, one hears the sound of the train.* MANGA, *fully drunk by now, is stacking wood in his house.*)

CHORUS: The bulldozer runs over the poverty of the poor
The bulldozer runs over the education of the children
The bulldozer runs over the hearths of the women
Over Baba's shelter
Bulldozer, Oh Bulldozer

The corporation's bulldozer!

(*Suddenly,* MANGA *begins to throw all his vessels outside. His wife tries to stop him. His neighbours watch him, others keep busy with their own work.*)

RESHAMIYA: Have you gone mad? (*Catching hold of his hands*) Our home is going to be destroyed tomorrow and you are raving drunk.

MANGA: (*With a vessel in his hand*) Let go of my hand.

RESHAMIYA: No, I will not let go. What has happened to you?

MANGA: I tell you, leave me. Or else.

RESHAMIYA: Or else, what? Will you beat me? Beat me as much as you want. Vent your anger on me, but I will not let you damage our home and belongings.

MANGA: You bitch, you will not listen to me…

(MANGA *begins to hit her. Pulling her by her hair, he takes her inside the shack.*)

RESHAMIYA: (*Crying out in pain*) Oh! Bastard! Let go of my hair… let go of me…

(*People gather outside* MANGA's *house.* MANGA *begins to thrash* RESHAMIYA *brutally with a stick. People try to rescue* RESHAMIYA. RAMSARUP, PAKYA, MUKESH *and* RAMYA *try to intervene.*)

RAMSARUP: Manga! Let go of Reshamiya. Have you gone mad? I say, let her go…

(*The people succeed in breaking* RESHAMIYA *free from* MANGA's *hold.* MANGA *looks like he has turned into an animal. Completely drunk, he is senseless. Her hair disheveled,* RESHAMIYA *wails loudly.*)

RESHAMIYA: Hey, beat me…beat me, you son of a bastard… I don't know in the company of which dogs he drank today.

RAMSARUP: Reshamiya, keep quiet.

RESHAMIYA: Why should I keep quiet? (*Begins to weep*) What have I done to deserve such beatings from this bastard? I just told him not to hurl our vessels outside. What did I do wrong? I go out to beg the whole day and then return only to get beaten up by him at night. He does not earn anything himself, and whatever I earn, he wastes it all on alcohol. Bastard!

RAMSARUP: Reshamiya, I told you once. Be quiet.

RESHAMIYA: (*Gets up and walks towards* MANGA. *The women around try to hold her back.*) No, I will no longer sit quietly, uncle. Today, I will die by his hands. (*Trying to free herself*) Let me go… let him beat me… let me test his strength…. Hey, why have you stopped? Hit me, bastard! Hit me! (*Screaming, she breaks down.*) It is better that I die once than live to die every day. (RESHAMIYA *cries.* MANGA *stands quietly to one side.*) Oh bastard, before hitting me, you should have at least spared a thought for the child that has been growing inside me for six months. What if something happens to our child? But you don't care.

MANGA: (*Breaking his silence.*) It is the thought of our child that led me to do this. (*His speech is slurred.*) I know that tomorrow morning you will hasten to save whatever little we have and dash into the crowd. In tomorrow's rush, the police and the corporation people will hit whoever comes in their way. What will you carry with you tomorrow? Your household or the new life inside you?

(*Both husband and wife burst out crying. Their belongings lie scattered. Everyone is silent now. A song is heard from backstage.*)

Beautifying the cities is the bulldozer!
Making children shiver in the cold.
Crushing people's dreams is the bulldozer.
Bulldozer, bulldozer.

## Scene Nine

*(Sounds of smashing are audible. There is a commotion in the settlement. The officials of the municipal corporation and the police have arrived with the bulldozer early in the morning.* RAMSARUP *and some other people have gathered. Some police constables and corporation workers are removing the wooden poles on which the shacks stand.)*

RAMSARUP: Sir, have mercy. We are poor ghumantoos. Where will we go? We have found shelter here with great difficulty. Where will we go if you drive us out from here also?

OFFICER 1: You say you are ghumantoos?

RAMSARUP: Yes, sir.

OFFICER 1: Then remain ghumantoos. Why have you burdened us by building illegal shanties here? Now listen, tell your people to remove all their belongings from their houses or we will bulldoze them out.

RAMSARUP: *(Pleadingly)* Please do not commit such an atrocity. Where will we take our children in such biting cold? Have mercy, sir. Have mercy on at least the children and the old people of our settlement.

OFFICER 2: Look brother, we are not doing this of our free will. We receive orders from the top. Your houses have been demolished on several occasions. Yet you keep rebuilding them every time. You simply don't leave the place!

RAMSARUP: Sir, we do odd jobs around this settlement. We sell maps near the railway station, the Rajbhois move around here, cleaning ears. the Bairagis sell toys on the railway platform and the Waghris sell vegetables in the market nearby. If we go to a new place, who will allow us to stay, who will give us our livelihood?

OFFICER I: The government does not care about all this. We want to clear this street and connect it to other routes so that buses can ply here. We plan to build two bus stands here.

PAKYA: But sir, if buses start moving here, what will happen to our children? If a child comes under a bus and dies, who will bear the responsibility?

POLICE INSPECTOR: Shut up, stop this nonsense. Go away or you'll be beaten up, you bastard. Remember, you are living here illegally.

RAMSARUP: How is it illegal, sir? Once there was nothing here, this land was barren, there was neither this bridge nor the new school nor this cemented road. We came and settled here back then, some forty years ago when this place was a jungle. People were scared even to pass by here for fear of robbers.

POLICE INSPECTOR: Oh, so those dacoits were you people. What else can you do other than steal? Even today you people snatch bags and chains, and pick pockets at the railway station. Leave this place or I will arrest all of you.

MUKESH: Sir, we work hard to earn our livelihood. We do not get to enjoy the freebies that you do.

POLICE INSPECTOR: (*Angrily*) What? What did you say? You called me a bastard (*He hits* MUKESH *with a stick. Everyone is scared now.*) Your mother…

(MAYURBHAI *walks in.*)

MAYURBHAI: Hey! What's happening here? (*Making his way through the crowd*) Move away… move…

RAMSARUP: Oh, it's good that you have arrived, Mayurbhai. You know how long we have been living here. We have seen you grow since you were a child. Please convince them to not demolish our settlement. Or we are sure to die in this winter.

MAYURBHAI: Look Ramsarup. You are the headman of this settlement. It is you who will have to persuade the residents to vacate this place.

RAMSARUP: (*Taken aback*) But why? We have been living here for decades. Why should we leave this place?

MAYURBHAI: Were you people here in 1976?

RAMSARUP: Yes, in fact, we have been settled here since 1960.

MAYURBHAI: Do you have the 1976 government order to occupy this space? Any document to prove this?

RAMSARUP: How would ignorant and illiterate people like us know about or have any legal documents?

MAYURBHAI: If you don't know, then quietly leave this place. This land belongs to the government.

RAMSARUP: (*Somewhat angrily*) Did this place not belong to the government forty years back? Why did you allow us to settle here at the time? You should have moved us then. We would have continued to wander. At least, we would not have had to see this day!

MUKESH: We have submitted several petitions to the municipal corporation, but so far we have not received any reply. Earlier, we used to receive a legal notice to vacate this land. Why have we not been issued such a notice this time?

MAYURBHAI: The government is not your father's servant to answer your applications! And please understand very clearly that it is the order of the supreme court of this country that all illegal constructions should be demolished immediately. There is no need to serve notices in such cases. Do you understand?

PAKYA: Mayurbhai! You made such promises in election time! That you would provide us with houses, install electricity and water facilities in the settlement, that all houses would have electricity connections. What happened to your promises?

MAYURBHAI: (*Enraged*) Hey, you! Who are you to remind me of my promises? I very well know whom you have voted for. (*To the* MUNICIPAL CORPORATION OFFICER) Come, finish your work quickly. I have to drop my children to school.

OFFICER I: Come on, move. Go ahead and begin the demolition!

(*Chaos! Someone is seen running with his belongings, another is gathering vessels, somebody rushes to pick up his bed, another is seen moving hurriedly with children sitting on his shoulders. The police are rushing everyone out. They wield lathis to scare the residents. MUKESH, PAKYA, RAMYA, MANGA and RAMSWARUP rush homewards.*)

MUNICIPAL CORPORATION WORKER: Hey. Pick up your belongings, or we will take all of it away.

A WOMAN: Have mercy, sir. I will take them in a minute.

*(As soon as she and her husband move to take their belongings, a municipal worker swiftly removes their cot.)*

RESIDENT: Oh sir. We are gathering our belongings. Why are you taking our cot away?

MUNICIPAL CORPORATION WORKER: We gave you time, didn't we? Since you did not remove your belongings in time, we are now entitled to take away all this stuff.

WOMAN: We have only two hands. How do you expect us to carry our children, our household and our cot all at the same time? Please, give us our cot back, sir. How will our child sleep in this cold winter?

MUNICIPAL CORPORATION WORKER: We don't know all that, you can come tomorrow and collect your belongings after paying the fine.

RESIDENT: Please, don't do this to us, sir. We are taking our things. Please! Please give us our cot.

MUNICIPAL CORPORATION WORKER: You won't get it. If you like, go and speak to the boss. Now go away.

*(Before their eyes, the bulldozer runs over their belongings. Both burst into tears. The children begin to cry.)*

CHILD: Baba… baba… my house… my house…

## Scene Ten

(MANGA's *house*)

POLICE CONSTABLE: Come on, get out of here or the bulldozer will crush you.

MANGA: Whose mother do they think has nurtured us that they threaten to run the bulldozer over us?

POLICE CONSTABLE: Hey drunkard! I just need to strike twice

on your head with my lathi and your buzz will evaporate.

RESHAMIYA: No, sir. Please forgive him. He has a habit of rambling. We gathered our belongings last night. Look, look over there...

POLICE CONSTABLE: No. You cannot keep your things there. Pick up your things and vacate this place. You cannot keep your things anywhere in the settlement.

MANGA: (*Angrily*) If we cannot keep our things on the roadside here, then where do we go? To the police station? If we keep them on the railway platform, the railway police threaten us that they will set it on fire. Where do we keep our belongings?

POLICE CONSTABLE: (*Throws his lathi at* MANGA.) Go to hell, for all I care. Why are you shouting? Hurry up or I'll arrest you both. (*He runs after them swinging his lathi.* MANGA *and* RESHAMIYA *gather their things and run, when suddenly* RESHAMIYA *falls down in pain.*)

RESHAMIYA: (*Writhing in pain*) Oh... Manga... Manga...

(MANGA *throws everything aside and rushes to* RESHAMIYA.)

MANGA: Oh Reshmi! Reshmi, what happened? I told you, oh god, come get up.

POLICE CONSTABLE: You are still here! Vacate this place... Run...

MANGA: Bastard! (*Angrily*) If your mother had to run carrying you in her womb and had she given birth to you on the streets, you would have realized what is happening. (*To the* POLICE CONSTABLE) Come, come here! Look here... look... (*Pointing to* RESHAMIYA *who is writhing in pain*) This anguished woman is your mother and you are the child she's carrying in her womb. After a few days, like thousands of children, this woman will give birth to you on some anonymous roadside and you will be crying on the streets. Do you understand now?

(*The* POLICE CONSTABLE *stands aghast. Behind them the bulldozer razes* MANGA*'s house.*)

## Scene Eleven

MALA: Oh sir, where are you taking my cot? Where will my old mother sleep? Have mercy, sir. My mother will die in the cold. (*The municipal worker takes away the cot.*) Oh, may God curse you! Not only have you destroyed our hut, you have taken away our only cot. May your mother also suffer as my old mother. Goddess Jogmaya will see to it.

(MUKESH*'s house is next door. The police and municipal people move towards his house.*)

POLICE CONSTABLE: Hey, vacate this hut. Be quick. The bulldozer is coming this way.

MUKESH: (*Comes out with his wife and daughter.*) Sir, please show some mercy. Look, my daughter has chicken pox… her whole body is covered with spots. She is crying in pain. Where will we go if you destroy our home?

MUNICIPAL WORKER: Please forgive us, brother. But this is an order from the big bosses. This is why… otherwise we will lose our jobs….

(*The bulldozer razes* MUKESH*'s shanty to the ground. One can hear the wails of the children and women. There are sounds of things shattering. People are shouting.* MUKESH *is seen walking away slowly with his daughter and wife.*)

## Scene Twelve

*(It is night. The residents are sleeping on the pavement. Some of them have kindled a fire to keep themselves warm. Their belongings are lying around, scattered.* PAKYA, MUKESH, RAMYA *and* MANGA *are sitting near the fire.* MANGA *is drinking liquor.)*

MUKESH: The bastards have razed the entire settlement. They beat us up. This place has turned into a graveyard.

PAKYA: This is the tenth time in the last ten years.

*(A dog's wail sounds out. Everybody's attention is drawn to it.* MUKESH *gets up with faltering footsteps and hurls a stone.)*

MUKESH: Hey, go away. *(The dog lets out a frightened wail.)*

MUKESH: *(Throws another stone)* Quieten this bloody dog. Of all days he had to let out his bloody cry today! We already have enough sadness and now he has come to announce death! Go, run away! *(Throws another stone. The dog's wail dies down.* MUKESH *sits down.)* Bastard. These dogs have become like the government. They start barking anytime, anywhere, at anyone.

PAKYA: Why are you cursing the dog? This is the fault of our fates.

RAMYA: *(Frightened)* I feel like Lord Yamraj, the god of death, is stalking us today. That is why this dog is wailing. I have heard that dogs can see Yamraj.

PAKYA: *(Frightened to* MANGA*)* Manga, I think, it is your turn today. It seems even Yamraj will not spare you today.

MANGA: I will not hand myself over to Yamraj so easily. I'll offer him a drink and win him over.

*(All four burst out laughing. Suddenly,* PAKYA*'s wife enters in alarm with her one-month-old child.)*

SEEMA: Hey, Pakya... Pakya... Pakya....

*(Everyone gets up hurriedly. Hearing her calling, even those who are asleep, wake up.)*

PAKYA: What happened? What has happened? Why are you shouting? And Munna…?

SEEMA: Yes, Munna. (*There are tears in her eyes.*) My Munna. Look how cold he is. Why is he not moving his hands or legs? What has happened to him? Please look at him…

*(Tears well up in* PAKYA*'s eyes.)*

PAKYA: (*Taking* MUNNA *in his embrace*) What nonsense are you talking? What has happened to Munna? Hey Munna… Munna…. Why has his body become so stiff? (*Crying*) Mukesh, please see what has happened to my Munna….

(MUKESH *takes* MUNNA *in his arms. As he tries to listen to his heartbeats, the dog rents out a loud wail.* SEEMA *screams.*)

## Scene Thirteen

*(It is morning. Some of the residents are gathering wood and plastic from the debris of the incident. All their possessions are lying around. Two children—one of them is planting a seed and the other is putting together a broken toy—are having a conversation.)*

CHILD 1: Hey, how did your brother die?

CHILD 2: I don't know. He was playing at night. He even held my finger. But then he died.

CHILD 1: But how did this happen?

CHILD 2: Father was saying it was very cold at night. His body became as hard as wood.

CHILD 1: Like wood… How did it happen?

CHILD 2: I told you! It was extremely cold last night.

CHILD 1: Did your mother not wrap your brother in warm clothes?

CHILD 2: How could she? The municipality people took away our mattresses, sheets, vessels, everything. They did not leave behind anything. There isn't even any food to eat.

(PAKYA *is taking his dead child, wrapped in a white sheet, to the cemetery. The residents go with him.* SEEMA *is crying uncontrollably. The other women try to hold her back.*)

SEEMA: Oh, where are you taking my child? Munna... my Munna.... (*Taking* MUNNA*'s body in her hands*) How can you leave your mother like this? My son... I bore you for nine months. You should have at least allowed me to love you to my heart's content. When the municipality people came, everybody ran with their belongings. I had to carry our belongings with you inside me. I protected you for nine months in my womb and you decided to leave your mother in such a hurry. At least you should have allowed me to look after you. My heart! At least you should have allowed me to hold you. Oh bastards, you could have at least left some warm clothes for my son.

(*She breaks down, wailing.*)

CHORUS: Beautifying the city is the bulldozer.
Children are shivering in the cold, O bulldozer.
We are mourning the death of our children, O bulldozer.
Crushing our dreams is the bulldozer.
Better than the entire world
Is Hindustan, our Hindustan
We are its nightingales,
It is our garden and abode
Better than the entire world
Is Hindustan, our Hindustan
Better than the entire world...

*(During the span of a few months, when this play was being produced, eight ghumantoo children died of extreme heat, bitter cold and heavy rains. Ahmedabad was being transformed into a mega city.)*

# 3

# Who am I?

Kushal Batunge
Edited by *Henry Schwarz*

My name is Kushal Batunge. I am eighteen years old and I study literature at L & C Mehta Arts College in Ahmedabad. I have been working with Budhan Theatre as a volunteer for five years. I am also a filmmaker. In 2011, I met Dakxin Chhara, who introduced me to the craft. Now I have three films to my name: *A Day in the Life of Ramchandra (Thief)*, *The Cremator* and *The Widow's Home*, and a Pepsi advertisement as well. Two other films, *Azaan* and *A Junior*, are still in the works. I work with Dakxin's company, Nomad Movies Inc., with Budhan Theatre, and with the production house, Room No. 20, as a filmmaker and a theatre actor.

## My Parents on My Choice

My parents and my uncle were always worried for my future. For them, my wanting to become a filmmaker was a mistake. It is a career for big people, they reckoned, and felt that I will never be able to earn money from it—an understandable sentiment. They have seen so many people from our community, who have tried pursuing a career in film or theatre, leading a difficult life. They made it a point to express their unhappiness whenever I left for rehearsals or to shoot films. Sometimes I felt that it is not films they had a problem with but with me—that they didn't have confidence in their own son. My cousin is a singer, a profession that is equally precarious, but his family was not worried. Maybe because my family was financially better off they thought that I would not be able to live up to their standard of living if I became a filmmaker. They could not believe in me because my choice was unfamiliar to them. I couldn't justify myself either because I did not make a good living. But it was not possible to earn well in the early stages, and I needed support.

I tried to find a job, but there were no vacancies. Wherever I went, they said, 'We do not have work, so how can we employ you?' So, I have stopped looking. I work independently and make films wherever I can. One day people will come to me and ask me to make films for them, or at least that's what I hope. Many people in my community pass hurtful comments about my career and my choices. Sometimes I feel very discouraged. Sometimes I feel bad that I can't earn enough money. But I try not to think about these things and just keep working.

## Bootlegging

My mother has been a bootlegger since her marriage twenty years ago. My father, Vijaykumar Batunge, was an advocate in the metropolitan court of Ahmedabad. He became a lawyer because he did not get a job as a teacher. He was from a poor family, but his father gave him an education and a house. Life, however, was always difficult—father worked hard before he got married and then for some years after. He married the daughter of a rich thief. They quarrelled a lot. She was accustomed to a comfortable life, but my father couldn't provide for that.

When he got his BEd degree, he worked as a teacher in schools and as a private tutor. He also did other odd jobs. He would sing in the commercial music bands of Chharanagar and in the company of his friends. This was when he started drinking heavily, but he kicked the habit when he started studying law. He thought that becoming a lawyer would be beneficial. Our community, classified as a 'criminal tribe', is known for thievery and bootlegging. Perhaps this was the reason why my father became a lawyer, so we could be considered respectable. As for me, I am not enthused by criminal activity either—it brings no profits, only losses on top of losses. Even after getting his degree, things were difficult for dad. He faced much discrimination in finding work. He would often sit alone at home.

Money was tight, and mother started selling liquor. Our house was mortgaged for twenty lakh rupees to supplement this. The business caused many personal problems. The customers who come to drink, from the city or other localities, are quite high-handed and there is constant fighting and quarrelling. First, she sold on the roadways, then at railway stations and then she began home delivery services. She took care of all of us. Meanwhile, dad kept looking for work in the court to no avail.

Seven years into his practice he developed a pain in his back. He took pain killers for a few days but they were ineffective. Eventually the doctor diagnosed him with cervical spondylitis. He was forced to leave the legal profession. I think that was when he gave up completely. He started drinking every day. It was not an expensive habit because he could drink the alcohol mother made at home. But then the entire burden of running the household fell on my mother. She became the father, so to speak. She had to work harder than ever before. And slowly her earnings increased quite a lot. So much so that she began selling alcohol directly from our home.

But the fact that her children were seeing the ins and outs of her business nagged at her—the noise, the quarrels. She decided to buy a new house from where she could work and keep us all away. This turned out to be bad decision and the beginning of the end for us as a family. Now father became less and less involved in the business. It felt like his life was becoming meaningless as he wasted away without work or reason. Mother began having an affair with an outsider. News of this spread like wild fire in my community. The judgement continues to haunt us even today.

My father fell ill, both mentally and physically. He developed a seizure disorder, and then one disease after another took hold of him. He grew frustrated. He tried to reconcile with mom many times, but she was not willing to change. Even I tried talking to her on several occasions. Once I even got into a physical fight with the two of them because I knew that these developments would ultimately mean the death of my father.

One Sunday morning I woke up at eight and was getting ready to go to the Chharanagar library. I brushed my teeth and went to my father's room to get a towel. He was sleeping as was usual with him. When I came back from the bathroom, I noticed that he was now lying awkwardly, like a wounded animal. His eyes had rolled back into his head. I tried to shake him awake, but he was already dead. I still don't know what happened to him. Seizure or what? I don't know. Many people in my community continue to blame my mother for his death. Even I feel that way sometimes. But I don't say it. My life has become empty without my father's love. He was the only person I really loved. He was my best friend. I can't help but think that either my mother or a seizure killed that man. Or both.

## Today

After father's death, our life has taken a turn for the worse. All our decisions have backfired, and there is no one to help us. My mother doesn't understand me. She is happier with her partner, the partner whom I blame for the death of my father. She has taken out a second mortgage on our first house, the one my paternal grandfather left us. She is also planning on renting out some of the rooms in our house so we can earn some more money. But the house requires repairs, and she cannot get that done because she is broke. People from the community embarrass us about the money we have borrowed. Even my cousin, who is well-educated, warned my mother that she would lock us out of our house if we didn't repay the twelve thousand rupees we owe her immediately. We are living in tough times, but we don't show it because in my neighbourhood you don't show your weaknesses to your neighbours.

## Future

I think Chharanagar is a treasury of stories. In the future, many creative and talented people are going to rise from this community and they will receive much acclaim. I too am a bright and successful documentary filmmaker and not too bad a person, if I may say so myself. And I am only one among many like me. Yet people in our community find it so difficult to have even modest dreams. I will keep fighting for the constitutional rights that have been guaranteed to the DNTs and will try to rectify the life of my community. I want to travel the world and understand and learn from different cultures. I hope that the world and the people around me will support me. I have lots of dreams for my community, my family and Budhan Theatre. And a day will come when we will be well known for establishing such a creative community.

# 4

# The life, livelihood and aspirations of a DNT couple

M. Subba Rao

This is the story of Pativada Satya Narayana and P. Chinni, a couple from the Mondi Banda community from the state of Andhra Pradesh, who make their living collecting and selling honey. The Mondi Bandas' traditional occupation involves the collecting of human hair and turning it into decorative material. They also create hair extensions known as savaram which are popular among South Indian women. Crow meat is a part of the modest Mondi Banda diet.

## Childhood

Satya Narayana is the eldest son of Pativada Satti Raju, an alcoholic vagabond who used to while away his time roaming around and picking up quarrels in the town of Samalkot, some eleven kilometres from Kakinada in East Godavari district. Satti Raju would often declare that he was from the upper caste called Kamma and that he had run away from home, that he was forced to live on the street as a child. Satya Narayana betrays a hint of pride when he relates how his father was a rowdy whom everyone in Samalkot was afraid of.

Satti Raju's wife was from the Dasari community, which traditionally sold cosmetics like vermilion and turmeric along with small hand mirrors, kajal and handmade combs of wood and buffalo horns. She used to carry her wares in a basket and sell them on the streets. Satti Raju used to visit her in an abandoned warehouse that was previously used to store mangoes.

Satya Narayana's mother lived with a group of homeless people, most of whom were from DNT communities. Satti Raju would come visiting every time he wanted money for alcohol and inevitably a quarrel would erupt. He would beat her up, then he would eat and drink and sleep heartily before leaving in the morning.

Satya Narayana and his younger brother were both born in the disused mango warehouse. Soon enough their mother contracted vaginal cancer and was forced into begging so she could make ends meet. One day when Satti Raju was thrashing her to extract money, she fell on the katti peeta, a hardy curved knife fixed on a stand used for cutting vegetables while sitting on the floor, and was killed instantly. Satya Narayana was seven.

The two brothers became destitute and ended up at a railway station where they would beg near the canteen for food. Soon Satya Narayana got a job washing dishes in the canteen and later he graduated to selling tea in trains.

## Youth

For fifteen years Satya Narayana worked as a tea vendor. In that time, his brother died of HIV/AIDS. Satti Raju was an absent father through all this. For all intents and purpose, Satya Narayana was an orphan—he worked and slept on the platform, drank cheap liquor, ate bhang and visited sex workers.

He first met his wife Chinni at the Samalkot railway station. She had just arrived in town with her mother to make a new life. They were from Yeleswaram village situated on the plains, nestled between the forests that dot the East Godavari district. Chinni's father had exclusive begging rights in the villages of the Yeleswaram mandal. This hereditary right, bestowed by the community heads of the villages, is called mirasi. It ensured that no one else from the community could enter these villages. Each family contributed twenty-five paise per annum and Chinni's father earned some four to five rupees a day. Her mother also worked with human hair and made decorative pieces to sell in weekly markets.

Chinni's father used to carry a knife and a musical instrument both made out of iron. The instrument was a ring with a long piece of metal attached to it. He would play it as he sang and begged for food, with his dry bottle gourd shell, hung by a thread and used as a utensil. This had been the community's traditional occupation for generations and he did not know any other means of earning a livelihood.

The knife was used to make cuts on the body and draw blood—this gained the sympathy of people. Another practice of the Banda community involved vomiting in front of the houses of potential donators and then picking up pieces from the vomit and consuming it. This caused nausea among the people and spurred their donations. In Telugu, 'Mondi' means obstinate, pig-headed, and 'Banda', insensitive. Popular wisdom is that when a Mondi person comes for alms, he will not leave until you give him something.

Chinni had three sisters and two brothers. Young men from another DNT community called Yerukala offered to marry the girls by promising in writing to join the community. But a few days into the marriage, they began harassing the sisters, forcing them to inherit Yerukala customs. The girls left their husbands and returned to their parents. By then, Chinni's father had contracted tuberculosis. He died the same winter. Soon, Chinni was also diagnosed with tuberculosis and had to leave her infant son from her previous marriage with one of her sisters.

## Marriage and children

Chinni and her mother left their village and made their way to Samalkot, looking for a better life. It was then, when they reached the railway station, that they met Satya Narayana. Their marriage was fixed after Chinni's mother negotiated the terms with Satya's vagabond father. It was an oral agreement to live together as man and wife, along the lines of a live-in relationship. By that time, Chinni's tuberculosis had cured to some extent. Satya Narayana rented out a hut for a hundred rupees per month, but soon the owners asked them to vacate. They had heard the husband and wife fight every day—Satya Narayana would get drunk and beat his wife up. Chinni could only scream helplessly. The landlords wanted no part in all this.

For a while they lived in the Samalkot station compound and then on the platform in a makeshift tent made of rags. Later, they moved to an abandoned plot along the railway tracks. The couple lived here for fifteen years and had five children. Over time, Satya Narayana grew tired of his life as a tea vendor. When a colleague was hit by a speeding train while selling tea, his disenchantment turned more resolute. He started looking for different kinds of work. The entire family moved to Rajahmundry in this pursuit and they pitched a tent on a street near the Godavari railway station, on the banks of the Godavari river. They lived there for three years and gave birth to two more children. In 1990, the couple moved with Chinni's brothers to Kakinada, in the East Godavari district.

## Honey collection

Satya Narayana knew how to climb trees and extract honey without being attacked by bees. In Kakinada, he began work as a honey collector. Along with Chinni, he collected one kilogram every day, and mixed it with two kilograms of sugar solution. He sold this mixture as pure honey, parading it about town with the hive on full display. Satya's father, Satti Raju, also came to live with them at this time. They all lived in a tent set up on the street. Satti Raju was by then gravely ill, and in 1995 he passed away in Kakinada's government hospital.

Then the city began expanding and a large number of trees were lost to concrete jungles. Common land vanished.

Life became hell for Satya and Chinni. Private land owners did not allow them to collect honey anymore. The two then moved to Yelswaram, where they pitched a tent along the compound wall of a government hospital. The children begged for food in the village, and that is how the family filled its stomach for a while. In the meantime, Yelswaram, which was a village panchayat, was upgraded to the status of a municipality. And people like Satya Narayana were forced to vacate their makeshift home.

## Homelessness to home owning

After they were kicked out, the family scrambled for a place to live. They temporarily pitched tent in a vacant lot in a lepers' colony. Adjacent to this was another colony where the Denotified Mandula community had settled. They were traditional herbal medicine makers and pig breeders. A priest from the local church told Satya Narayana about an abandoned house that had been donated by someone to people afflicted by leprosy. They could move in there, he said. The family lived there for six years. But then one day the owner of the house returned, and they were forced to vacate once again.

On the advice of the priest, Satya Narayana approached the revenue department and appealed to them that he was from a DNT, a nomad, and had no place to live. At the time, the officer of the department was under immense pressure from the higher ups to complete the given target for family planning and birth control operations. So the official promised Satya Narayana a plot of land to build a house on condition that he undergo a birth control operation. Satya agreed. A plot was allotted to him and on it he built a hut with Palmyra leaves. The family continued to extract and sell honey.

The owner of the house in the lepers' colony, who had evicted them, meanwhile came with an offer to sell it to them for ten thousand rupees. After selling some more spurious honey, he collected enough money to become the owner of a second house—this one too with no doors, no flooring and the walls not plastered. The government's low-cost housing scheme then gave Satya financial assistance of fifty thousand rupees to build a pucca house. But the whole process was terribly mismanaged. The contractor made mischief in the supply of building materials and the construction took some four years to complete. Satya joined a chit fund to finance the building of the house.

## New conditions

Satya Narayana takes his surname 'Pativada' from his father who is of the Kamma caste. In the then joint state of Andhra Pradesh, Kammas and Reddys held the majority of land holdings. In spite of his lineage, Satya Narayana remained a DNT. The landed community never considered him as one of them. His mother and wife both were from DNTs, and for all practical purposes he was a Mondi Banda man.

Of his nine children, two died due to undiagnosed illnesses. Now he has five daughters and two sons. Two of his daughters are married and have children, but neither lives with her husband. Their husbands both belong to different communities. Satya Narayana's stepson, Gouri, from his wife's previous marriage lives separately but works with the family collecting honey. He is a chronic alcoholic and suffers from severe leg pain.

The family now owns two auto rickshaws to haul their equipment from village to village in pursuit of beehives. The children are unable to attend school as the family moves about—but the girls are the worst affected. It is unsafe for them to be left at home and while on the move they face much sexual harassment.

## Social status

Satya Narayana's community is considered the lowest among the low, looked down upon even by the Scheduled Castes. Nomad DNT girls are considered desirable and are openly bought and sold. They are harassed routinely, and DNTs, who are categorized as Backward Castes, enjoy no legal protection equivalent to the SC/ST Prevention of Atrocities Act.

Once when Satya Narayana's daughters were out shopping, they were harassed by some passing SC youth. Chinni and Siva, the eldest son, went to the police but could not get their case registered. But Siva did not relent and he kept up his efforts to get justice. In 2014, he was murdered by three of the accused's friends. The National Commission for DNT Human Rights then took up the issue and organized a fact-finding mission. The offenders were arrested but were out on bail soon enough. They are now threatening the family and offering them money to withdraw the case. One of them even offered to marry the girl they had harassed. It is clear that these youths believe that the DNTs are begging communities and do not deserve any respect.

Although the family is still fighting the case in court, they lost Siva, an important part of their occupational set-up. He was an expert at climbing trees and extracting honey. Their second son, who is less than fifteen years of age, cannot climb trees. The family's livelihood is in jeopardy again. They tried to enroll the girls into a government school by approaching the district collector, but the family could not bear the expenses. They got their third daughter married off in a hurry, while the other two daughters have dropped out of school, and joined the honey business.

## Now

Satya Narayana suffers severe pain in his testicles and suspects that he has edema and kidney stones. However he cannot afford an operation. He has lost all sensation in his left leg and cannot feel anything, not even a pinch: it's like the limb doesn't even exist. But he continues consuming bhang and cheap liquor. Chinni never recovered fully from tuberculosis and became drug dependent. She still suffers from bouts of cough and fever, and is an asthma patient. She lives on medicines, and is bedridden when she doesn't take them.

Satya Narayana and Chinni want the killers of their son to be punished severely. They want the future of their children to be bright and without the daily struggles they faced; they should not have to struggle for food and clothing. But owning property is not a big part of this aspiration. They do not think of it as a necessity. They have no other plans for the future—all they desire is to roam about freely in search of honey and to die peacefully.

# 5

# Story of a hero who broke the fence

Bhimrao Jadhav

*Translated by Chandrakant Puri*

This is a translation of an excerpt from Bhimrao Jadhav's *Katha Kateri Kumpanachi* (1998; Pune: Chandrakala Prakashan), a book which was originally published in Marathi. Popularly known as 'Guruji', Jadhav is a prominent leader of the Nomadic and Denotified Tribes in Solapur, Maharashtra. He created history by asking the government to break down the fences erected by the British and de-notify the ex-criminal communities of India.

*

My name is Bhimrao Jadhav. People call me 'Bhimrao Guruji' because I am a teacher. I was born on 19 February 1923 in a family from a criminal tribe called Bhamta. In the days of their rule, the British notified our tribe and condemned us as born criminals. As a child, I never understood the meaning of Bhamta. Only later did I learn that the name was given to us because it was deemed that we were all involved in theft and dacoity. But no one in my family ever did anything criminal. It always puzzled me why the brand of criminality was associated with us. Just because one was born in a particular caste?

Under the British, all our communities condemned as hereditary criminals were concentrated in one location, which was surrounded by a fenced wall. This is where I was born. Our locality was kept under strict surveillance. If someone needed to cross the fence, to go inside or out, an official permit was required. Women weren't even allowed to cross the fence, as they were kept in check both by the Britishers and the men of our community. While most of our relatives lived in villages, our settlement was near the city. I used to visit my native village, Dahitane, during summer vacations. There I would see many of my community members involved in crimes. That was the era of gang wars between different villages and tribes. Though they looked like fights between entire villages, they were actually just feuds between two families from criminal tribes who were made to fight against each other. The role of each tribe was predefined by people from upper castes, who considered it their right and our duty to protect them. Many people from my community died in this bloodshed. They considered it a matter of pride to die for their village. My uncle, Satva, too was of this ilk—his four young children were always on the ready to pick a fight with anyone.

I remember stories from childhood of an incident when the neighboring village had planned an attack on our village on a new moon night. They knew that Satva was away visiting an ailing relative, so they descended on our village to settle an old score. We were tense—our protector was absent. When the village head found out that Satva was missing, he sent a group of people to get him back. We kept waiting but he was nowhere in sight.

All the women and children were asked to stay indoors. The men in the village were getting ready to fight. Young boys collected stones and some were armed with guns. At around midnight, an announcement rang from the opposite side, 'Prepare to die'. And it began. Within the first few minutes of the skirmish, two people from our community died. We were stricken, hoping against hope to come out of the attack alive, when suddenly we noticed the other side had stopped. They were screaming now. In the dark, none of us could make out what had happened. Just then someone announced that Satva had arrived. We heaved a sigh of relief. The hero of our village had arrived, had caught our enemies unawares and had attacked them from behind. We lost two people, but they lost seven. The village celebrated the victory, and Satva was welcomed with much pomp.

The hero of our village had survived several attacks and protected the village, but as he grew older, his children moved to other small towns. Satva and his wife were left alone in the village. The hero who had for so long been hailed and taken care of became a liability on the village. Satva died as a burden to all.

There are many such stories about people from our communities. Those of us who were in settlement camps were forced to perform labour as per the instructions of the British police. British missionaries often came to our settlements to visit our families. They taught us prayers and spread awareness about Christianity. If we didn't sing these prayers, they would punish us. Also taught in our settlement were music and drama. The teachers for these disciplines were very good and they worked us hard. I participated eagerly in the drama classes that happened in our neighbourhood. Our family was particularly strict when it came to going to school. If I missed even one day, my father would punish me severely.

After the British left, the school I went to was handed over to Balutai Khare, a renowned freedom fighter and writer. With her in charge, we started getting lessons in nationalism and community development. We also began collecting information about criminal tribes for our teacher. Balutai went on to write a novel called *Bali* based on this information. In it, she wrote about a character resembling my father. For her, it was surprising that my father was not involved in any criminal activity despite belonging to a 'criminal tribe'. Balutai always cared for me and gave me special attention because of my father's reputation. It was because of her that my friends and I began creating campaigns to increase awareness about our communities.

The missionaries, on the other hand, forced us to convert to their religion. Since I did not give in to their wishes, they stopped providing me with financial help. My father's earnings were meagre, so I had to stop attending school. I got a job as a labourer in a factory. Father was deeply pained by this. In 1942, following Mahatma Gandhi's call, I participated in the freedom struggle. We wanted freedom from the British in the hope that if they left India, our miseries would end.

Unfortunately, our miseries persisted even after

independence. We were still considered criminals and treated as notified tribes. I decided to enter politics. It was time for action. I was elected as councillor from the Solapur municipality and then as a mayor. It was a great opportunity for me to initiate change in my community. I implemented several development projects to improve our economic condition and was appreciated for my work. But I was disheartened to see the persistence of the stigma of criminality that I was working against.

Nevertheless, I kept trying to change the situation with the help of friends and a few politicians. Eventually, we approached Jawaharlal Nehru, who was the first prime minister of free India, and told him that though India was independent, our community was not. Sympathetic to our cause, he promised to direct the then chief minister of Maharashtra to do something to improve our condition. After a lot of persistence and persuasion at the central and state levels, the government of Maharashtra finally passed a law for the decriminalization of criminal tribes on 13 August 1949. The law minister came to cut the fence around our settlements. However, the bigger challenge still remained: would society move past their prejudices against us? My struggle to end this discrimination continued.

I remember an incident from when we were lobbying for an Act to help get rid of the stigma of criminality. We had gone to meet the personal assistant of a minister, and were waiting for him near his chamber. I was still the mayor of the municipal corporation. When I sent a paper with my name and details asking for an appointment, he told the people seated in his office that he was about to meet the representatives of criminals. When we heard this, we marched into his office and asked him to apologize to our entire community since as per the law, we were not criminals anymore.

Though the government had set us free, it had not planned any policies or programmes for the rehabilitation of ex-criminal communities. I was developing residential schools, forming collective spinning mills, cooperative farming, and micro enterprises for the development of my community members, while also working hard to reform the community's 'jaat panchayat' (the traditional customary dispute resolution system) which was unjust to women and the poor. My contribution to community building was acknowledged and I was selected as head of the jaat panchayat. I used this as an opportunity to change the mindset of my own community.

The barbed wires have finally been taken down, and the horizon of our thoughts is slowly widening. It has been a long road of struggle and determination. But it is only half-travelled and the destination is still far away. I am grateful to all those who have been part of my journey. Ahead lies a more difficult path. Our goal, however, is clear to us, and the new travellers are ready. I wish to end my narrative here, with a sense of satisfaction, and in the hope that the journey towards reclaiming our rights and dignity will be fulfilled.

# 6

# Pata

Kanji Patel and Rupalee Burke

Translated from the Gujarati by *Rupalee Burke*

*Pata* (Rail Tracks) is the dramatic avatar of three short stories centring round Denotified and nomadic communities of Gujarat, India, from the collection *Dero* (Camp; Rangdwar, 2008) by Kanji Patel. The songs in the play are adaptations of Kanji Patel's poems published in three collections—*Janpada* (Vicinage; Sahacharya, 1991), *Dungardev* (Mountain Deity; Gujarati Sahitya Parishad, 2006) and *Dharti na Vachan* (Earthspeak; Purvaprakash, 2012).

*

*Pata* (Rail Tracks), directed by Dakxin Bajrange, was first performed by Budhan Theatre at Diamond Hall, Gujarat Vidyapith, Ahmedabad, in September 2014, with the following cast:

SUTRADHAR: Dakxin Bajrange
PATEL I: Atish Indrekar
KANU CHAMTHA: Sahil Bangali

PATEL 2: Sonu Bangali
PATEL 3: Siddharth Garange
RAMESH CHAMTHA: Krishnakant Macchrekar
MULJIBHAI: Vikas Bhogekar
SARPANCH: Kushal Batunge
CHILD: Shubham Bajrange
VOICES BACKSTAGE: Budhan Theatre Team

*

AMBAIDAS: Kushal Batunge
HARJIVAN: Sahil Bangali
BHOLA: Atish Indrekar
SOMA NAT: Sonu Bangali
PATEL 1: Vikas Bhogekar
PATEL 2: Siddharth Garange
PATEL 3: Abhishek Indrekar
RANCHHOD: Arpit
JAMADAR: Krishnakant Machhrekar
JIVLI: Amisha Indrekar

*

SERVANT: Vikas Bhogekar
GAMJI: Atish Indrekar
DHIRKI: Sheena Sunray
SAKHIDAS: Kushal Batunge
SAKHIDAS' WIFE: Kalpana Gagdekar
BHUVO: Krishnakant Machhrekar
BEAT GUARD: Sonu Bangali, Vikas Bhogekar
POLICE: Sahil Bangali

## Mahabharat

### Scene One

(*The* SUTRADHAR *enters at the beat of the drum and takes centre stage.*)

SUTRADHAR: Greetings friends. Budhan Theatre, Chharanagar, presents before you the play *Pata*, depicting the plight of the nomadic communities of Gujarat. It has been their fate to be victims of tyranny. Oh, how they fought against foreign rulers. And now they fight against their own countrymen. Are these nomads, wandering for centuries, not citizens of this country? What terrible oppression this is! We begin with the Mahabharat of the Chamthas. It is a Mahabharat which is not performed, but is lived on a daily basis in villages across Gujarat.

(*Riding his camel cart, singing a local folk song,* KANU *enters stage. A* PATEL *enters from the other side.*)

PATEL I: Hey there, Chamtha, your camels have turned pricey we hear.

KANU: (*Bowing at the feet of the Patel*) How can that be, Patel sir? It is only recently that we have switched over from donkeys to camels for livelihood. We have been earning our bread in your reign for years.

PATEL I: (*Sarcastically*) I have heard that you are slightly literate.

KANU: (*Modestly*) I studied up to class two. By then our tents had moved elsewhere. Can read and write very little. Can count a bit.

PATEL 1: (*Arrogantly*) Anyway, what use is studies to nomads like you? Now listen. I have a shipment that needs to be taken to the city. How much will you charge?

KANU: The city is fifteen kilometres from here, sheth. I'll charge five rupees a maund.

PATEL 1: Have you lost your senses? Not five, I will give you three rupees.

KANU: This camel has cost me ten thousand rupees. The cart costs as much. We can't even feed the camel if we charge three rupees.

(*Four Patels gather.*)

PATEL 2: (*Approaching* KANU) My, my, Chamtha, will you bargain with us?

KANU: But sheth…

PATEL 3: (*In an intimidating tone*) No ifs and buts. We will pay two rupees a sack.

KANU; (*Imploring*) I will take four rupees instead of five if you say, Kalukaka, but two rupees is far too less. We haven't kept that much margin.

PATEL 2: Look Kanu-da, you may charge five rupees from people of other villages, but from us you will have to charge two rupees, do you understand?

KANU: Sheth, I know I am a small man, but you are forcing me to cross my limit. I can charge four if not five but definitely not two.

PATEL 3: Looks like these wretched folks are growing insolent. They will have to be driven out of our village.

KANU: (*Falling at the* PATEL*'s feet*) Sheth, don't be so harsh on us. Where will we poor folk go?

PATEL I: (*Kicks* KANU. *he falls to the ground*) Go wherever you want. Undo your tents tomorrow morning and get going.

(*Saying this the Patels exit.*)

CHORUS: Vira mine, somebody hews your hill, re
Vira mine, somebody sucks your sea, re
Vira mine, somebody sucks your sea, re
Rivers and forests once mine, air my refuge, re
Rivers and forests once mine, air my refuge, re
Gone now are my name and my village, re
Citizen of this country, I am Adivasi, re
Citizen of this country, I am Adivasi, re
Solitary I wander transient, re
The sun on my head, I eat my rotla, re
No home, no school, no livelihood, re
My sons beg in a distant village, re
Oh how my heart is pounded, Oh my life, re

## Scene Two

(MULJIBHAI, *a noble Patel from the village, is seen sitting with the Chamthas in their tent. He is promising them a way out.*)

KANU: Tell us Muljibhai, did we do something wrong? How can we afford to charge two rupees when everything costs so much these days?

RAMESH: Muljibhai, where will helpless folks like us go with our children?

MULJIBHAI: Kanubhai, don't worry, I care for your community, that is why I have got your ration cards, election cards and Aadhar cards made. We will meet the collector tomorrow.

(*They exit.*)

CHORUS: Wanderers of the land
We eat the yield together, re
Griddles heated, children separated, re
No land beneath, only the sky above.

## Scene Three

*(The Patels have gathered at the village square. They are engaged in discussion with the village headman, the* SARPANCH.*)*

PATEL 1: Sarpanch saheb, I have heard that Muljibhai, a Kanbiya of our village, has helped these Chamthas to obtain ration cards, election cards and Aadhar cards. He has also got their names entered in the BPL list.

PATEL 2: No! This means these bloody Chamthas have a stake in the village. The scoundrels have firm roots now.

SARPANCH: Don't get ruffled, brothers. We will have to set these good-for-nothings right after all. The nomads have the audacity to strike bargains with us. Their tents are on our pasture land which we acquired from the forest department. I feel that if we grease the district forest officer's palms, he will kick these fellows out of here.

PATEL 3: Then what are we waiting for? Let us go ahead.

*(They exit.)*

CHORUS: From the time the sun, moon and sky were made,
The forest has been ours, re
The water is ours and so is the land
Vacate the forest, build roads,
Dig square pits, we are told, re
We do the labour you want us to
But at least spare us our loin cloth, re
You accuse us of devouring forests

Damn it, are we not human beings?

**Scene Four**

(*Night at the Chamthas' settlement. Spotlight on* KANU. *He is reading out the forest officer's notice.*)

KANU: "I, the Round Forester, D.C. Bhabhor, hereby serve this notice to you, Kanu Khoda Chamtha and your fellow members for illegally occupying forest land on the outskirts of Dodiya village. You are ordered to vacate the land within ten days of receiving this notice. If you do not obey the order, legal action will be taken against you." (*Breaking down*) I had hardly imagined these Patels would go to this length for the sake of a mere two rupees.

MULJIBHAI: Kanu, you have done nothing wrong. It is your right to earn your livelihood.

RAMESH: I fail to understand how this piece of land is forest territory. This is the pasture land of the village. The village school is built on it. We have even been paying panchayat taxes to stay here.

MULJIBHAI: Take heart. The collector has permitted you to stay here on the basis of the documentary evidence. I will meet with the forest officer once more. I too am a Kanbi Patel. I will not rest until I have ensured your right to stay here.

(*Feeling assured, they all exit.*)

CHORUS: Our labour is our capital

Our sweat our wages, re

The Kharvan fisherwoman curses the sea, the Agariya starves for salt, re

Nat, Vadi, Luhar, Sansi, Koli, Bhavaya, Nayka, re

Saraniya, Maldhari, Vadar, Kangsiya, Halpati, Charan, re
Mashanjogi, Ghantichor, Bhamta, Vanjara, re
Vansfoda, Madari, Turi, Raval, Chhara, Chamtha, re
Show us at least one paper that protects the helpless, the fragile and the Earth, re

**Scene Five**

*(The* SARPANCH *and other Patels flock to* MULJIBHAI*'s house at 10 pm to discuss the Chamtha issue.)*

PATEL 1: Muljibhai, you are a Patel, why are you out to crusade for this worthless lot?

MULJIBHAI: Why are you out to shatter the peace of the night? Do you know the ancestors of these very Chamthas fought against the British? That is why they were branded as criminals. Even after independence we haven't allowed them to settle, earn their living and acquire education. There are two hundred such communities in our country today. The advent of the railway spelt doom for their traditional occupations. They now hop from one source of livelihood to another. Now both the government and their fellow citizens shun them.

PATEL 2: (*Curtly*) We aren't concerned about all that. Their donkeys and camels plunder our fields. They wash meat and fish at the village handpump. How can we tolerate all this? Do these wandering nomadic thieves have papers permitting them to stay in our village?

MULJIBHAI: (*Determinedly*) You are accusing them falsely. Let the government decide what to do about them. Please calm down.

PATEL 3: Muljibhai, you seem to be on their side. You may recommend the case of the Chamthas to the government, but keep in mind, we want them out of our village.

(*The Patels stomp out of* MULJIBHAI*'s house.*)

MULJIBHAI: Who knows whether these people will ever understand the plight of nomads? Will they ever develop an ounce of humanity?

**Scene Six**

(MULJIBHAI, KANU *and* RAMESH *are seen standing together.* KANU *is on the verge of tears.*)

MULJIBHAI: Kanu, we will write a letter to the Human Rights…

KANU: (*Interrupts*) Arre, what human and what rights? The forest department staff have demolished our tents and taken away our belongings. What are they going to do with them, boil and eat them?

MULJIBHAI: Calm down, Kanu…

KANU: (*Agitatedly*) Kaka, how can I be calm? When we went to take back the wood, the officials asked for the bills. We had bought the wood from the Patels of the village, we were not given bills.

(*A* CHILD *enters and starts reciting the national pledge.*)

CHILD: "India is my country. All Indians are my brothers and sisters. I love my country and am proud of its heritage." Bapu, I have to recite it in school tomorrow.

KANU: Recite it dear, recite it. (*The* CHILD *exits.* KANU *mutters to himself.*) "Are my brothers and sisters…. am proud of its heritage."

MULJIBHAI: I am worried about his schooling.

KANU: The powers that be are always going to listen to influential people. We nomads have no right to education. Our children want to study. We want honest work and we want to settle down. But we are destined to lead a nomadic life.

RAMESH: (*Ruffled*) Wonderful! Because we didn't agree to charge less, the village land has become forest land. Salutes to such laws. Woe upon such a society and government.

KANU: Ramla, our nomadic communities are far too young compared to these sedentary societies. It is our ill-luck that the society and government keep us hungry so that we spend our entire life making ends meet. Generations have gone to waste in this pursuit, Ramla, and we don't own even a measly stretch of land. Our days in this village are numbered.

RAMESH: But Kanu, despite having all the papers...

KANU: Yes, despite that. These Patels will not allow us to stay. If we persist, the forest department will not spare even our belongings.

RAMESH: What will they get by uprooting poor labourers like us in the middle of the monsoon season? Is law made for men or are men made for law?

(*Noise of belongings being damaged. Angry voices.* "Get out of here", "Leave immediately", "Are you going or shall we break your legs?", "Out... Out", "Get lost".)

VOICES: (*Backstage*) The canal is two hundred feet away, don't go there.

VOICES: If you settle by the lakeside, we will drive you away in the dead of night.

KANU: (*Dejected*) Hey, come on, let us move our tents elsewhere.... Settle for a while and then get going again....

CHORUS: The tempo moves, the forests sway

Track formed across the field, re

My mountains sway

My trees uprooted

(*Other Chamthas join him, and taking slow steps they move in a circle on stage before they exit. The* SUTRADHAR *enters as they exit.*)

## *Bhoin* (Land)

### Scene One

SUTRADHAR: Friends, you must surely have seen young Nat men, women and children performing amazing acrobatic feats on the street to earn their living. These feats qualify as begging in the eyes of the law. The British have left, but their laws are still in force in independent India. The Nats who were once performers have now sadly come to be branded as thieves. We present before you the plight of Soma Nat in the second piece: *Bhoin,* Land.

(*It is night.* AMBAIDAS *is peering around with a lantern held high.*)

AMBAIDAS: It looks like the monsoon is going to be weak this year, again. Paddy and maize yields will suffer. The crops are close to harvest. These are the days of staying vigilant at night. We are going to have a famine on our hands. The fields will resound with cries of 'thief, thief'. The bloody Nats from the village outskirts will surely create trouble. Now, how is an old man like me supposed to keep vigil?

To hell with everything. Now, it is up to fate whether my crops will be safe or not.

(*Two Patel youths enter.*)

HARJIVAN: Is something the matter, Ambaikaka?

AMBAIDAS: It is a bad time, boys. The bloody Nats are at the village outskirts. Every day we hear of how crops are getting stolen from the fields.

BHOLA: Ambaikaka, we will be on guard. You go home and sleep in peace.

AMBAIDAS: (*Relieved*) Oh, it is good to have boys like you in the village.

**Scene Two**

(HARJIVAN *and* BHOLA *are seen keeping night vigil in the fields.*)

HARJIVAN: Hey Bhola, give me a beedi, it will help pass the night.

(*Suddenly they hear strange sounds in the field.*)

BHOLA: Harji, be silent. Hear that? I think somebody is passing through the field. Must be a paddy thief. (*Shouts.*) Everyone, now! Nab him, nab the thief.

(*Some Patels come rushing in with* SOMA.)

SOMA: I haven't come to steal. I didn't find a vehicle to go home, so I was crossing the field.

PATEL 1: You bloody thief, stop where you are or I'll break your legs.

SOMA: (*Mutters to himself*) These Patels will kill me. I must escape somehow.

(SOMA *tries to escape but is nabbed by the Patels. One of the youths recognises him.*)

PATEL 2: Oh, it is Som-lo Nat-iyo. Take him to Ambaidas!

SOMA: (*To himself*) These fellows have recognised me. A trip to the jail and a thrashing for sure. Even if I escape, the Kanbiyas will be at my door with the landlord. (*Aloud*) Believe me. I had gone to Kothamba to my sister-in-law's house. I returned so late because I had work to attend to at home.

PATEL 3: Tear the rascal to shreds.

(*The youths bind him with a rope and drag him to* AMBAIDAS*'s house.*)

CHORUS: Spent a lifetime with onc loin-cloth
Playing with pickaxe and spade, re
When famine strikes, we block our doors with brambles,
Leaving villages, wander in the city of smoke, re
Can forests be saved, can rivers be kept alive, re
If just one tree survives, if the wind stays hearty
Sweat poured to build high-rises is worth it, re

## Scene Three

(*The house of* AMBAIDAS.)

BHOLA: (*Knocking*) Ambaikaka… Ambaikaka, open the door. You have a guest.

(AMBAIDAS *steps out of the house.*)

RANCHHOD: It is me, Ranchhod. We have nabbed a paddy thief from your field.

AMBAIDAS: O, ho ho ho. So this is my guest, hmm? (*Punches him*) Smash every single bone in his body. (*Kicks him*) Today we'll show these Nats what happens when they steal from the fields of the Patels. (*He asks for his hunter-whip and starts lashing Soma.*)

SOMA: Sheth, let me go. I was returning from my sister-in-law's house. I am no thief, sheth.

AMBAIDAS: I don't care if you have stolen anything or not. The fact that you had dared to set your dirty feet in my field makes my blood boil. (*To* BHOLA) Go, call the Jamadar.

(*The* JAMADAR *enters.*)

AMBAIDAS: We have caught a thief, sir. He has been stealing paddy from our fields daily.

JAMADAR: (*Kicking* SOMA.) Which community are you from?

SOMA: Sir, I am a Nat. I am not a thief. I labour for a living.

JAMADAR: So you are a Natiyo. (*Slaps him.*) I knew the moment I saw you that you are a nomad. Your flexible body will be of great use in jail.

AMBAIDAS: Their women beg during the day and these thieves come out at night. Drinking liquor and producing children is all these goons know.

(JIVLI, SOMA*'s wife, enters.*)

JIVLI: Sir, let my Soma go. He had gone to my sister's in Kothamba. Since he didn't get a vehicle to come back, he was walking home.

JAMADAR: Shut up, Nat-di. Looks like you also want to go to jail.

JIVLI: Sir. I swear my Somla will not step into anybody's field ever again.

SOMA: (*Chiding* JIVLI) Jivli, don't you fall at the feet of these Kanbis. God has written imprisonment and contempt as the destiny of us Nats. (*To the* JAMADAR.) Beat me as much as you want, but do not say nasty things about my community. I haven't created this community. Communities like the Kanbis have created it. (*In a rising tone*) Born nomads, we are fated to wander from one village to another. If we enter the village, the Patels drive us out. Despite the fact that our ancestors drove the white rulers out of this country. (*Determinedly*) Jivli, you go home while I go to jail to ask my friends how they are doing.

(*Fade out*)

CHORUS: The entire burden on the poor fool's head
Bound always to explain, re
When bridges collapse, when the river is infuriated
When the Earth is incensed, when forests go dry
All on his head, no choice but to plunge
Prisoner of an open prison, you poor fool, speak now, speak.

## *Pata* (Rail Tracks)

### Scene One

(*As the song ends, the* SUTRADHAR *enters at the beat of the drum and addresses the audience.*)

SUTRADHAR: Naiks were performers in bygone days who earned their living by playing the bungal and performing the bhavai in Gujarat. With time the traditional theatre form was snuffed out of existence and the Naiks lost their livelihood. Gamji Naik is a performer turned labourer, he is a woodcutter. Left with no choice, Gamji takes up a weapon not for destruction but for creation, for reconstruction.

(*About four or five huts of Naiks on the outskirts of the village.*

*Some men are lying drunk on charpoys, some are indoors eating.* SAKHIDAS*'s servant enters the scene.*)

SERVANT: Hey Gamji, why do you drink liquor every day when you don't have enough to eat? It will be the cause of your demise. Sakhidas has called you to chop down trees in his field.

GAMJI: (*In a drunken stupor.*) We drown our sorrows in liquor. When we don't get food, all we can do is tuck our legs into our stomach and lie still.

DHIRKI; (*To the* SERVANT) He'll come tomorrow morning. (*To* GAMJI) Go, so you can earn a few rupees. I need to buy clothes for the children and myself.

GAMJI: The avatar of Nayakda is a cursed one. If you steal, the government gives you food. And if you labour, the sheth gives you food.

(DHIRKI *goes inside the hut. Somebody starts playing the drum, singing*:)

Lo, lo, the hill is aflame
Vanjara re
On the bank of the Anhela
Lo, lo, on the bank of the Anhela
The kalal brews liquor re
Vanjara re

(GAMJI *dances in an inebriated state. Fade out.*)

**Scene Two**

(*Next morning at* SAKHIDAS' *house.* SAKHIDAS *spots* GAMJI *at the threshold.*)

SAKHIDAS: O, ho ho, Gamji, here you are at last. (*To his wife*)

Bring tea for Gamji.

(SAKHIDAS's *wife brings tea in a khakra leaf bowl for* GAMJI.)

GAMJI: How much work is to be done? I hope to finish before the noontime sun is overhead.

SAKHIDAS: (*Drinking tea out of the saucer.*) Half a day's work. One neem and one har to be chopped, that's all. (SAKHIDAS *watches* GAMJI *and asks, after a thought*) Gamji, where are you originally from?

GAMJI: (*Blowing smoke out of his mouth.*) Roaming the hills all over the land, we stayed where we could. Neither my father nor I have any clue where our ancestors came from. When we are not sure of our present, how are we to be sure of our past?

CHORUS: Vira mine, wind and forests sliced, gone our roots and fields, re

Later came scales, wooden handles fitted to axe-heads, re

Farming snatched, labour emerged, eating, drinking and hunger followed, re

Plains, mountains, rivers, boulders gone, boundaries of lakes broken, re

Resolutions of man and forest annulled, gone are name, home and livelihood, re

## Scene Three

(SAKHIDAS *and* GAMJI *in the field.*)

GAMJI: One and a half times five seers for the neem and four or five seers for the har.

SAKHIDAS: Ten seers for the neem and five seers for the har.

GAMJI; I don't understand how much is ten seers. I'll work

only if you give me what I have asked for, sheth.

SAKHIDAS: I said ten seers for the neem. Now, are ten seers more or one and a half times five seers? You won't find such a generous person as me. By the way, what do you do for work the rest of the year round?

GAMJI: We extract honey, chop wood, pick kalli bhaji from the hillside, sell datan in return for grains or money. Somehow, we manage to pull through the year.

SAKHIDAS: Alright then, get started.

(GAMJI *fixes the blade of the axe on the wooden handle and starts chopping.*)

CHORUS: Later came scales, wooden handles fitted to axe-heads, re

Farming snatched, labour emerged, eating, drinking and hunger followed, re

(*A monitor lizard springs out of the hollow neem trunk and coils itself around* GAMJI*'s leg.*)

GAMJI: Oh my! It's a monitor lizard!

SAKHIDAS: Oh no! Everyone, come running! A monitor lizard has grabbed Gamji. Ramesh, Suresh, Naresh, hurry, we must take him to the bhuva.

(*They carry* GAMJI *to the* BHUVA.)

BHUVA: (*To* SAKHIDAS) This is no ordinary monitor lizard. It has been possessed by a ghost. We need to perform a ritual. Listen, I will need a vermillion cloth with golden borders, four coconuts, five kilos bundi and fifty rupees in cash. Do you agree?

GAMJI: Oh god! From where will I bring so much money? No... no....

SAKHIDAS: Bhuva-ji, don't worry about the expenses. I will

pay for the things. You begin the ritual.

(*Picking up a peacock feather broom, the* BHUVA *strokes* GAMJI*'s body with it and mutters chants. Amidst frenzied drumbeats, the* BHUVA *enters a trance. His body shakes violently. With his companions, he makes strange noises to awaken the Mataji till she finally enters his body. He talks to the Mataji while appearing to talk to himself.*)

BHUVA: Mataji says 'unless you give me an offering, the ghost won't leave his body'.

SAKHIDAS: We will give whatever offering the Mataji demands.

BHUVA: (*Stops shaking*) Hmm.... Take this man to the hospital and call me when the offering is ready.

(GAMJI *cries out in great pain as he is being taken to the hospital.*)

**Scene Four**

(GAMJI *is taken home.* DHIRKI *is shocked to see him in his injured state.*)

DHIRKI: Oh god, how did this happen? (*weeps*)

GAMJI: Oh Dhirki, a monitor lizard sprung out of the hollow trunk of the neem tree and got me.

DHIRKI: Gamjii, working with the axe is worthless. There's not a morsel in the house, and now we'll have to repay the sheth.

GAMJI: Dhirki, what will I do if I give up this work?

DHIRKI: Now I will have to go out and earn. That is the only way.

GAMJI: Don't you dare even think about it. And put a leash on your tongue. I am man enough to earn a living. (GAMJI *starts flinging whatever he can lay his hands on towards* DHIRKI. *She walks out cursing* GAMJI. *It takes a while for* GAMJI *to calm down. Then suddenly he realises what he has done.*)

GAMJI: Hey Dhirki… where are you? I promise I won't hurt you. Dhirki….

(*There is no response.* GAMJI *feels very uneasy.*)

The forest department does not give us work. If we sell wood or vegetables, they arrest us. We have no land to till. Even if we manage to get some coal from firewood and try to sell it in the city in the dead of night, they wait in stealth to arrest us.

(*Tired,* GAMJI *falls asleep.*)

CHORUS: Huge trees of poison grow, oh sister
Lakes overflow when I weep, re
Wretched husband I have to tolerate, oh sister
Heartless destiny has ruined my life, re
Hungry children clamour for food, oh sister
Empty vessels tumble in the house, re

## Scene Five

(*Next morning* GAMJI *starts for the city with a sack of coal on his shoulders to sell. A beat guard standing at the entry point to the city nabs him.*)

BEAT GUARD I: Stop. Or I will thrash you. Come on…. Come with me to the station.

(GAMJI *throws away the sack of coal and tries to run but is caught by another beat guard. They take him to the forest police station.*)

## Scene Six

(*In the forest police station.*)

BEAT GUARD 2: (*To the police*) We have caught him with a sack of coal, sir.

POLICEMAN: (*Hitting* GAMJI) It is against the law to burn wood from the forest and sell coal. When you stay without food and water for ten days here, you'll get to know whether you are a Naik or Joriya Bhagat.

BEAT GUARD I: Joriya Bhagat, who is he, sir?

POLICEMAN: Joriya Bhagat is their ancestor. He fought against the British a hundred and fifty years ago. He belonged to Jambughoda. Mind well, this is Swaraj, not British Raj. The law will be swift even on your father, even if you are Joriya Bhagat's descendants.

(*The forest police exit.* GAMJI *tries to stand up but cannot due to the pain in his leg. He screams in agony.*)

GAMJI: (*Airs his woes*) Not an extra pair of clothing, nothing but coal to eat. From where shall I get food for my children? We are called forest-dwellers, but we get jailed for anything we do. We touch a tree and we are doomed. We don't dare to till the land. We left the hills behind to stay at the village fringes. My children take people's cattle to graze in exchange for a few pieces of rotla and two pairs of clothes a year. Which boulder shall I strike my head on? No matter how much liquor we consume, the intoxication wears off in no time. Only hunger haunts with persistence. We have no rights on the hills or the plains. We have created neither hunger nor begging. They are written in our destiny. Where has our kingdom gone? Where have our hills gone?

(*He starts weeping as lights slowly fade out.*)

CHORUS: Frolicking we came to the mountains
Wandering we came to the mountains, re
Children girdled at waist, hunger in bellies,
Encampments undone, thorns crushed, re

Doubting the nomad, trusting the sedentary
That is the way of those that reign, re
The twelfth generation of the agonized nomads
Lives the life of dogs and cats, re
Those who travelled across the earth to trade
Now beg, toil and drown sorrow in liquor, re

## Scene Seven

(*The railway track.* KANU, SOMA *and* GAMJI *enter one after another.*)

KANU: I am Kanu Chamtha. You saw how we were driven out from the village outskirts. For a mere two rupees.

SOMA: I am Soma Nat. I have returned from a two month's trip to the jail. Is it a crime to cross a Patel's field?

GAMJI: I am Gamji. I have spent three months in jail. These railway tracks are the cause of our nomadic plight. The British came here and went back by these railway tracks. We must smash them.

(*The trio start smashing the railway tracks. Gradually all the actors enter the scene and start smashing the railway tracks.*)

CHORUS: Smash the railway tracks, Gamjibhai
Smash the railway tracks, Gamjibhai
These railway tracks undid you
These railway tracks undid you
Undo the railway tracks and demand your dues
Undo the railway tracks and demand your dues
Gamjibhai.... Gamjibhai... Gamjibhai...

# 7

# Children of darkness

Dhruv Bhatt

Excerpt translated from the Gujarati *Timirpanthi*
by *Vishal Badhani*

When Sati woke up in the morning, she found her mother already busy with housework. She had spent the morning fetching water from a faraway source. The cooking would go on till afternoon.

On a cold and beautiful winter morning, the whiff of smoke rising from the danga, the gypsy caravan, is a pleasant sight. That, with the fresh aroma of a rotla straight from the firewood stove! Sati rose from her cot and embraced her mother from within the quilt which was still wrapped around her. As she pulled a tin box from under the cot, mother said with a little wryness, 'A hug?' Sati stayed mum and pushed herself away to sit at a distance. Presently Raghu also woke up. Before Sati could give her father some water, mother said, 'We need millet!'

Raghu replied in a drowsy voice, 'By tonight or tomorrow, for sure, Taapi.'

Taapi was clearly irritated. 'When will your tomorrow come? All the boxes are empty. Only I know how I manage this kitchen.' Although Taapi's exact words did not reach Raghu, her complaining saddened him. Normally, he would have scolded her for grousing on such a pleasant morning, but instead he said fondly, 'It was you who made me take an oath to not go to work during the day. Now you are repenting.'

Taapi let out a laugh. To amuse her, Raghu was speaking in the Narsi dialect rather than in Bhantu. This made Sati smile. Again, she went to embrace her mother, as if saying, 'In the entire danga—in the entire world—I have seen no one who laughs as sweetly as you!'

Sati looked into her mother's eyes and saw her smile fade away. Her face was pale now, as she took the flour out from the tin-box and heaved it into a large curved plate. Kneading the dough quite forcefully, she almost broke the clay pan while placing the rotla on it. Both Sati and Raghu knew what had affected Taapi's mood. She could not control her emotions whenever that thought crossed her mind, but expressed her untameable grief in unsuccessful ways.

Taapi had completely shut down when she learnt the truth about the fateful event. She could neither cry, nor speak, nor do any work. She used to sit staring at the sky. How could a mother come to terms with the death of her young son, a death caused for no reason?

On the day when Raghu and Taapi first set up their danga on the outskirts of a village in the Charotar region of Gujarat, a wedding was happening inside the village periphery. Without their knowledge, the couple's twelve-year-old son had gone to check out the event—to witness the music and the dazzling fireworks of the wedding ceremony.

Though Raghu's son had the potential to become a hattchaurak, a thief skilled at working markets and public gatherings, that day he had not gone out for work. He just wanted to enjoy himself. A watchman was guarding the gate of the wedding venue, so there was no point in going too close. The boy stood at a distance and observed people enjoying the glittering and lavish ceremony. When the watchman stepped away for a while, he could not resist the temptation of going closer to the gate.

That was when the bridegroom's family started whispering that the ceremonial bag for the bride was missing. It was the bag with all the fine clothes and jewellery for the bride. She could only attend the marriage rites after putting all of it on. Naturally, the people from the bridegroom's side began panicking. They started shouting that someone had stolen the bag. Such speculations were being bandied about wildly in the frenzy. 'He must be some bugger from the bride's village.' 'Go after him, he must be running into the nearby fields or on the road.' 'He is not likely to have gone far, catch him!'

Seeing the bustle, the boy upped his guard. He thought that if he stayed there any longer he was likely to fall into unnecessary trouble. He had never experienced getting caught but had heard a lot about it in the danga. Word was that one was spared only if he was handed over to the police, or else it could be fatal.

The advice passed down by ancestors and masters of the art is that in such situations the best thing to do is to run away as fast as possible. Even the scriptures advocate that a thief who carelessly gets into trouble is not supposed to pause at a place for very long. So the boy immediately took flight for the danga.

'Look, there he is running. He is the thief, someone catch him now,' a voice called out. The bridegroom's party, along with some villagers, came rushing out in hot pursuit.

They soon realized that no upper-caste boy could match the pace of someone from the Aadodiya tribe. They knew they couldn't catch him. Once he disappeared from sight, he would be gone forever. They began throwing stones, bricks and whatever else they could find to knock him down.

A villager coming from the opposite side who had seen the boy running, threw a stick at his legs, which knocked him down. The boy fell and before he could get up or even speak, the crowd began attacking him.

Wise men might use the word 'inhuman' to describe what happened next. But the word hardly captures the barbarity specific to humans. Those who witnessed the attack know that not even beasts or demons could do something so brutal. In the entire universe, only humans are capable of such inhumanity—with no second thought, neither reason nor concern.

As he was being thrashed, the boy tried to prove his innocence over the din of the crowd; even cattle could not have borne such pain. No one heard what he was trying to say. Nothing was clear, neither the boy's cries nor the crowd's abuses. Even the ceremonial bag became secondary, to the extent that nobody wondered why it was not in the boy's hand or anywhere around him. Only when the boy's screams died down as he lay in a pool of blood did someone have the pious thought, 'It will be a bad omen if someone dies during a holy ceremony like a marriage.'

Had someone not reminded them about the need to protect the piety of the event, they would have killed the boy right there. As the crowd began dispersing, someone came rushing to tell one of the groom's relatives, 'There is a phone call for you from your house, come quickly.'

The entire crowd followed him. As soon as he picked up the receiver, he was told, 'Funny people you all are! Leaving the ceremonial bag at home, you started off for the marriage and the bag is here. Now manage with whatever you have to keep up the ceremonial rites. We will have the other rites later. That is the most convenient thing to do.'

A ghastly silence fell over the crowd. Some of them felt guilty and openly regretted their actions. Others were aware of the problem they had invited on themselves in the form of a body lying outside the marriage venue. They began plotting what the most convenient path would be.

People on the bride's side assured them, 'Don't worry, we will find a way around this. There is great unity among the villagers. No one will let on to the police about what you did. The matter will be buried here. Our people will not utter a word; you please manage your folks.'

Very few bridal families have had the luck of witnessing a situation when the groom's party is utterly helpless. Such lucky ones should not miss out on saying whatever they wish to. They should grab the opportunity with both hands. Someone said, 'Is this how gentlemen behave? Without any common sense, any logic? Well, nothing can be done now. Let this be a story of the past and forget about it.'

The groom's father sat with his head lowered. Thankfully for them, the unconscious boy lying outside did not belong to the village. He was only from the danga on the outskirts. But there would be a stiff penalty for the village if they reported the matter or handed the wounded boy over to the danga. Once the Aadodiyas start shooting with gofans, their traditional leather slings, no one's head would be safe. Just drop him at a hospital and walk out quietly. We can deal with the rest later.

Meanwhile, the residents of the danga were searching for the little boy. They searched for him through the night. It was only the next afternoon that they learned of his hospitalization. Taapi and Sati spent two days in the hospital, huddling together, accompanied by tears, as they watched over their unconscious child. Neither the doctor nor the nurse knew what had happened to him. He might have been run over by a vehicle or fallen off a tree. Thankfully, a kind-hearted person had dropped this unknown boy at the hospital, otherwise he would have died on the road. The doctors tried to bring him back to consciousness while Taapi kept blessing the stranger who had saved her wounded son.

One cannot say who was more fortunate, Taapi or her son, on being liberated from the hospital on the third day. The kindhearted villagers paid the hospital bill. The constable, Mr. Khatri, turned out to be a good person. It was because of his intervention that the police did not trouble the villagers much and handed over the dead body.

After performing the boy's funeral rites late in the evening, the entire danga spent a restless night and got up early the next morning. Taking along their goats, dogs, donkeys and elders, they vacated the fields and started moving in search of a new place. Sati was about a year and a half old. She used to sit in her mother's lap and observe her crying and sighing. She was, of course, not aware of what was going on.

One of the scriptures probably says that the bigger the secret, the more likely that people would want to spread it, and thus more chances of it being revealed. In this case however, the entire village was extremely disciplined. And so Taapi consoled herself that her son had died a natural death.

Then came the rumours. The secret had travelled to another village, and then finally to the danga—the boy was neither run over by a vehicle nor did he fall from a tree. An investigation was conducted. And the truth was out. Taapi surprised herself by not shedding a single tear. She did not even abuse the killers. She did not speak for two days. Eventually, she declared, 'No more staying in the danga. The government has allotted us land in the city. It is fine if it is dirty and congested, without proper sidewalks and always under surveillance. We will stay there. So what if we are expected to report to the police station every day? In any case, I wanted my son to study. It is not like the police treat us better here. My son would have become a lawyer and taught them a lesson. Never mind. Now that my son is gone, I will get my daughter educated. Let our community criticize us, I don't care. That Tendra got educated, didn't she? I want to educate Sati. I want to leave this work. We will do whatever is available in the city. If nothing works out, we will brew alcohol. No one can do that better than an Aadodiya.'

All her relatives, including Raghu, tried dissuading Taapi. 'Our boy's life was destined to come to an end; he would have died some other way if not this.'

'Life has been worse. Don't you know your friend Godavari's story? Two of her maternal aunts died on the way from Sindh to Kutch because they could not find any water. Her mother survived, but the other two died of thirst. No one from the danga was able to provide water to the little girls. Godavari and her mother returned after burying both of them in the desert. If that was their fate, what can one do?'

From time immemorial, it has been a common practice for the living to think about the dead this way. Despite her relatives' many attempts to convince her, Taapi insisted on leaving for the city. For eight years she kept saying, 'As soon as we have some savings, we will buy a small house in the city.' There was no point in even discussing which was better, the city or the danga.

The day she found out the truth about her son's death, she made Raghu swear that he would never work during the day, only in the dark. There are hardly any people around at night. The few who are out and about are manageable. But during the day a whole crowd can gather in no time. Taapi was not ready to lose her husband like she had lost her son.

Sati had seen her brother die, but she did not know anything about it. Eight years later, she understood a bit more. The incident was discussed often at the danga. Taapi's son became a lesson, an example to stop someone from taking unnecessary risks.

Sati disliked the whole tragic bubble that came with her mother's unvented fury. She busied herself playing or with some other work. That morning, when mother complained that there was no millet at home, Sati grabbed a piece of rotla and took off.

Her friends were not around. Everyone was busy with something or other or just asleep. Sati tried making a toy out of some dry stems and twigs. God knows she had never seen the inside of a school, but she often played 'school' with her toys and taught them whatever she knew.

Soon Jasali came along and told Sati, 'Go and tell your mother that we are going for a bath in the afternoon. We have found a comfortable place to settle. There is a cistern near a well filled with water, and that too with a tap. Besides, there is a wall that provides cover.'

Sati ran back to inform her mother. Other women had begun assembling. On her way to fetch water, Jasali had taken permission from the owner of the place.

Kaavi said, 'I have already soaked soapnuts in water for washing our hair. We will also wash our clothes. Once we bathe the younger girls, we can take our time...'

Jasali suggested, 'Hey, bring your sickles. There are many fruit trees along the fences. We will get some on our way back.'

Everyone liked her suggestion. They would also make alcohol after a long time—some wine made of guava. They could even make wine from berries. When they were in the desert, they had to have wine made of jaggery or chemicals. This would be far better.

The younger girls were each given a bath and sent back to the danga. Once she had washed Sati's hair, Taapi asked her to go straight home and not to roam around. On her way back, Sati kept looking at the surrounding farms and fields. Millet was growing in one of the farms. Sati thought, 'It would be good if father could go there tonight. If someone goes now, the farmer will catch him. Then, my father will have to go in search of another farm, which would probably be further away. And he will get millet only if it is still in the farm. These crops are standing uncut because the owner had sown them late or because they don't have the time to reap them yet. Why else would a farmer keep ripened crop in the fields? By now the crops should have been threshed and put away in storage containers.'

The millet was still uncut because the farm did not have sufficient water. If the farmer had enough water, he would have wanted to grow some winter crops as well. He would have wanted to prepare the land at the latest by Diwali.

Sati felt refreshed after her bath and went close to the farm. She was entranced by the aroma of the ripened ears of millet. She daydreamed about popping roasted ears of millet straight from the coals into her mouth. All around her she saw the fields and woods in complete peace. The millet was almost double her height. It would not take much time to go inside and take some ears, would it?

The only problem was that girls and women do not do these things. It is understood that Nayaks or groups of thieves would never involve women in their work. Such work was not meant for them. A woman's job is to scout for possible targets to be looted during the day, help her husband set out for work, and then to hide whatever valuables he brings back. That's it. Beyond this, she is not entitled to any other work.

Sati thought it would be wonderful if some ears could be twisted and broken right from the top; but father had told her to never twist the ears of the crop from the top. The ear has to be chopped from its stem. It would be nice if a sharp sickle could be arranged. Suddenly, she remembered that they had carried sickles to the well. She made up her mind. Running back to the well, she secreted away a sickle and returned to the target farm. She looked around and cautiously made her way through the bushes.

It is not easy to steal crops during the day. The owner could walk out at any point. He could be watching over the crops from a distance. A farmer can easily sense even a slight change in the usual lay of his desired crop. Besides, the kusumaal, the thief who steals tempting things like flowers, would draw attention inside the millet crop: the millet-sticks that usually lean downwards immediately stand upright when they feel the touch of a thief. That is why a true artist has to tune herself to all the movements of the farm. One has to lean while working and move with the crop.

There are also birds like the luring larks who start chirping as soon as they see unusual movement. The red-wattle lapwing is another trouble maker; its constant tweeting always invites attention. There is no way out when it spots someone. Only when you take care of all these possibilities can you become an artisan of this work. Or you can run your stealing business in the dark. Even the silver mellow glow of the moon is dangerous. Scriptures have warned that a trainee artisan should be divabhit, one who is afraid of the sun.

Standing inside the farm, Sati was invisible to anyone outside. The wind found it difficult to reach where she stood. Sati moved the millet sticks delicately and chopped off the ears as she synched herself to the movements of the moist, dense and green crop. Neither the lark nor the red-wattle lapwing had the slightest clue that someone was right there in the middle of the farm. She had become one with the symphony of nature and time, totally present in the being of the field.

It is said that a true artist experiences oneness with her art a precious few times in life. Even if Sati had experienced such a state of meditation, she was not mature enough to understand it. But the little girl had created a world of her own in the farm. If someone saw her working, they would hardly believe their eyes.

Art that deserves whole-hearted appreciation is not limited to the stage, to concerts, or to art galleries or books. Art is universal. It is present in the woods, in deserts, in forests and in oceans, in outer space—everywhere. What artists are blessed with is just an atom of this unending, ever-present immediacy of art.

Sati filled as many ears as she could into the makeshift bag she had fashioned out of her skirt. She wished she could collect more, or at least as much as her mother needed, but she knew she could not carry so much back home. Quietly, she slid onto the main path from the bushes. It was a pleasant winter's day. A light wind was blowing, and Sati wanted this feeling to never end—the calm, the peace, the contentment. She put her next foot forward.

# 8

# Confessions of a Chhara actress

Kalpana Gagdekhar

Translated from Bhantu by *Roxy Gagdekhar*

On 31 August 1998, Ganesh Devy, Mahashweta Devi, whom we called Amma, and some other intellectuals came to Chharanagar for the first time, to visit me at home. Some Chhara youth, including Dakxin Bajrange and Roxy Gagdhekar, were also present. We mostly discussed how we could develop the Chhara community. Since we were the ones who had invited them, Dr Devy and Amma asked us what they could do for us. 'We want books to read,' I said. They were taken aback. Immediately, they resolved to set up a library in Chharanagar. Seeing our enthusiasm and potential to make a change in the community, they suggested we make a street play, a bhawai as we called it, on the life of Budhan Sabar and his death in police custody. On the day we performed the play, we saw positive media coverage of Chharanagar for the first time, as opposed to the usual pieces about thievery and liquor brewing.

Our first meeting was informal but it led to the formation of the National Convention on Denotified and

Nomadic Tribes, which held its first conference at Bhopal's Indira Gandhi National Museum of Man in December 1999. There we decided to celebrate 31 August as Vimukta Diwas, or Liberation Day for DNTs. All this led to the establishment of a national and international movement for all DNT communities. Devy and Amma have always inspired and motivated us to work for the development of future generations. Their efforts resulted in the creation of a National Commission for Denotified, Nomadic and Semi-Nomadic Tribes under the ministry of social justice and empowerment. We have been working for the community without rest ever since.

I had never imagined that I would have a career in the theatre and the arts. After our first performance of *Budhan* at Ahmedabad's renowned Darpana Academy, we received immense praise from the audience. People came to me after the performance, gave me warm hugs and congratulated me. I felt good in my soul! Many reputed newspapers interviewed me. I felt proud of what I had accomplished. Before, I was a shy and introverted person, I didn't interact much with other people. But my theatre and acting career unwrapped me. I began exploring things I would have otherwise avoided. I became confident when talking to other people. I discovered who I really was.

Ahmedabad is divided into two parts, east and west. Chharanagar is located in the eastern part of the city. I was always afraid to go west because the people there were more educated and well-dressed, and they saw us as 'born criminals'. For them I was a thief, a Chhara. The first performance of *Budhan* was in western Ahmedabad. Many intellectuals came to watch our show. To them it was the first time a Chhara 'gang' had entered the western part of the city for a good cause. After the success of this performance, we began getting invitations from all over the country to come and perform.

We have now performed in Delhi, Bhopal, Pune, Kolkata, Kochi and many other parts of India. Budhan Theatre has also helped us build international contacts, and interacting with them helps us change our perceived identity. We have met several influential people, from academics like Henry Schwarz and Kerim Friedman, to filmmakers like Shashwati Talukdar. Our members have travelled internationally and as we travel across the country and around the world, we are exposed to different people, with whom we can exchange our experiences.

For five years we gave repeat performances of the same play, *Budhan*, while simultaneously building our library and our networks, running many after-school and weekend programmes in literacy, homework assistance and theatre workshops in the library. This helped us expand our knowledge about world theatre. We also produced and performed a famous play by Badal Sircar called *Bhoma* (like *Budhan*, the title refers to an ordinary rural peasant who embodied poverty and injustice). When we were performing *Bhoma* at a local university, Dhirubhai Ambani Indian Institute of Culture and Technology in Gandhinagar on 10 October 2003, Dr Devy named our group 'Budhan Theatre'. That was an historic day for us.

One incident along this journey describes how my passion for theatre has changed my life. I was running late for a performance in Saputara once. I was also in the last trimester of my pregnancy. Somehow, with the help of Dakxin's youngest sister, who was performing with us, I walked a distance that normally takes an hour to cover in less than half an hour and reached the venue. Once we were there, the security forces recognized us as Chharas and refused to let us enter. Dr Devy, a well-known personality at the event, berated them. He said that if his troupe was not allowed to participate, he would not participate either. He then declared that we would perform on the streets in protest, to shame the people who had barred us from entering. Next thing you know, we were performing in Saputara before an enormous crowd. That incident cemented my commitment to street theatre and my belief in the power of people's expression.

These are some of the small ways through which we made our voices heard and showcased our skills to those in power. Budhan Theatre has led my husband, Roxy, to take up a career as a journalist with BBC News. It has taught all of us to identify the discrimination against our communities and has given us the tools to counter it. If Budhan Theatre had not existed, then my husband and I would not have achieved so much in our careers.

We have not limited ourselves to bringing about change only in our community. Dakxin Bajrange and I have fought for other DNT communities residing in Ahmedabad, such as the Dabgar, Raj Bhoi and Vaghari communities. These are former nomads who have been camping in the city for many decades, on what used to be their ancestral migration routes. There are at least 227 families who are struggling to get housing and livelihood in eastern Ahmedabad, where the

DNT communities reside. Towards this end, we have filed a case against the Ahmedabad Municipal Corporation. Dakxin took charge of filing the documents, and he filed hundreds of applications under the Right to Information Act. I on the other hand have been educating them through theatre, providing them insight about how they can fight for their survival and justice. This fight has stretched on for years. It was only recently that the Supreme Court allotted some plots for houses, giving several DNT families a place to live.

The judgement was historic in the present phase of the DNT struggle because before this the Supreme Court simply did not know that DNT communities existed. Now they officially recognize the existence of DNTs and their oppression. This incident was a major victory not only for DNT communities residing in the Maninagar settlement but also for all DNTs across the country. The Supreme Court has actually given them brick houses! Living in pucca houses has been the dream of every family in Maninagar that has lived under plastic sheeting for the last forty years.

Budhan Theatre also runs informal education programmes for the children of various DNT communities. Ahmedabad is engaged in a process of intense gentrification; to develop and beautify the city and its infrastructure, the government has demolished many DNT slums like the Maninagar settlement. We train people on how to raise their voices with the help of theatre, cultural activities and their traditional occupations in order to get justice. Budhan Theatre acts as a central body for the uplift of DNT communities from the grassroots level.

In 2005 we performed a play in one of the major police academies of Gujarat, the Karai Police Academy in Gandhinagar. Hundreds of police officers, from constables to IPS officers, saw our show that day. We gave them an anti-police play, but the police who watched it were moved and touched by it. They came to know our side of the story, and of our talent in theatre. Police Chief Keshav Kumar took the microphone in his hand and gave a heartening speech: From this day forward we will not view every Chhara person with suspicion, we will treat them with respect. That was the proudest moment of my life.

Occasionally we come up with big ideas to produce plays by foreign playwrights: like *The Lower Depths* by Maxim Gorky, *Death of an Anarchist* by Dario Fo, and Jean Genet's *The Balcony*. We have also produced environmental theatre in Maninagar, directed by the Bollywood actor, Mohammad Zeeshan Ayyub, who is a graduate of Delhi's prominent National School of Drama. Our play *Budhan* has been included in the curriculum of Georgetown University and many other colleges and universities around the world. We do not really aspire to have an international audience, because our efforts are focused on immediate changes close to home. But we are happy to receive international attention when it comes.

There are some ways in which having international recognition is beneficial. My husband Roxy Gagdekhar went to the United Nations in 2010 to speak about DNT communities to the Permanent Forum on Indigenous Issues. He met with the acting director of the forum, who promised to send a special rapporteur to Chharanagar. However, we are still waiting for that visit. In 2006, Budhan Theatre also sponsored a special programme at the United Nations under the banner of their Culture of Peace project. Minister Shashi Tharoor spoke eloquently about our demands. We still await the results of these findings, but we are patient people.

Nonetheless, BBC officials were impressed by my husband's portfolio and said that they were delighted to have him on their team because they believe in diversity and equality. At some point in my life I was neglected and discriminated against for being a Chhara. I was considered a born criminal. Budhan Theatre strongly identified the discrimination present in our society and effectively countered it in various forms. Our international profile works in unpredictable ways to improve our condition. Many international scholars have come to study our community and to provide assistance. Some of the benefits of having them here is that we get to practice our English, and send students for postgraduate work overseas.

Along with my work in Budhan Theatre, I became involved with a Gujarati language project where I go to play the role of Kasturba Gandhi, the wife of M.K. Gandhi.

When I got the role, I was terrified. I didn't know anything about Kasturba and her life, and Gujarati was not my first language. My son and my husband helped me tremendously to find information about Kasturba. I credit my ability to understand and become characters to my experiences at Budhan Theatre. I pulled up my socks and began researching as much as I could about Kasturba. She was completely different from Shyamali, the character I played in *Budhan*. And yet I found myself analyzing my past experiences and how I brought myself to play Shyamali. It was while working on *Budhan*, that I learnt how to build a play, how to research a character, how to get involved in the character, how to bring that character to life and how to put it out on stage.

*Kasturba* was a landmark play for me. After the show became a big success around the city and I became a celebrity, I was mostly known as Kasturba. In my professional life I have played the role of two extraordinarily strong women: Budhan's wife, Shyamali, and Mahatma Gandhi's wife, Kasturba. These two women have helped me recognize my potential as an actress and have taught me about the significance of women in society.

It is beyond belief that I have done more than a thousand shows around the nation with Budhan Theatre. With *Kasturba*, I have performed more than forty shows around the country. As it was a big hit, people started recognizing me. I started receiving attention from many news agencies, and my interviews appeared in major newspapers like *The Times of India*, *Divya Bhaskar* and *Gujarat Samachar*.

There was a time when Roxy and I were not financially stable, but we never hesitated to act in political plays. We were together with the community from the time of the establishment of Budhan Theatre and the Chharanagar library. We have faced great odds in our lives. Roxy and I used to sell milk in the evening to make a living. Sometimes we also sold snacks and vegetables. People used to say that the theatre had driven us mad and that we were irresponsible because we travelled around the country to perform, despite having no money to feed our children. We had to face several problems in our lives, but we were so inspired and motivated by Dr Devy and Amma that it kept us going.

Our motive at that time was to establish a platform for Chharas and for all DNT communities to voice their grievances at a national level. Our wish for the future is to provide education to the children of Chharanagar and other DNT communities so that they can represent themselves in the times that are to come.

# 9

# Budhan

Dakxin Bajrange
Translated by *Sonal*

## Characters

BUDHAN
SHYAMALI
JUDGE
INSPECTOR ASHOK ROY
ASSISTANT SUPERINTENDENT OF POLICE
CONSTABLE 1
CONSTABLE 2
CONSTABLE 3
VILLAGERS 1–3
ASHISH
SHOPKEEPER
GUARD
SRIDHAR
PRISONER

### Scene One

NARRATOR: Namaskar! Before we begin the play, let us glance at our history. Of the total population of a thousand million people in India, about six crore people belong to Denotified communities. For reasons unknown to anybody, we are singled out and forced to bear a burden.

We are the DNTs or Adivasis, the people belonging to ancient times. We have witnessed the changes taking place on earth for millennia. We live amidst nature. We are born in its womb and we die in its lap. We were once one with the jungles, but today we have to fight for our rights in the same forests. For centuries the DNTs have been killed. Earlier, when a DNT passed through a village, his body was cut into pieces.

(*A few tribals pass through the rear of the stage, carrying wood. A few persons hiding in the forest attack them. Their terrifying, pain-stricken cries for help fill the stage. The tribals are butchered. All characters stand still.*)

NARRATOR: In 1979, the people of the Lodha community were tormented and drowned.

(*The tribals are tied to imaginary trees as actors 1, 2 and 3 shout.*)

VILLAGER 1: Submerge their heads in water.

VILLAGER 2: Force them till they stop breathing.

VILLAGER 3: Torture them to death.

(*The heads of these tribals are plunged underwater. They die in agony. All characters assume their original positions.*)

NARRATOR: Nobody knows exactly how many people from Denotified communities are killed so brutally. Most of us are unaware of the atrocities being perpetrated on them. Rights are being snatched from the very people who rightfully own this country. We present to you the story of one such community, the Sabars. This is the story of Budhan Sabar, a young man belonging to the Sabar community who was killed in a police atrocity. We want change! We want a revolution!

(*Each character shouts for revolution and then all stand in single file.*)

CHORUS: There has already been one revolution and another is yet to take place. That was a revolution brought about by Bapuji. This revolution will be of the DNTs.

SHYAMALI: What you are about to witness is not the end but a beginning.

BUDHAN: This is Akarbaid, a small village in West Bengal. The law views the Sabar community living here as a community of thieves.

NARRATOR: In this small village, Budhan was living a quiet life with his wife Shyamali and their son.

INSPECTOR ASHOK ROY: But on 10 February 1998, Budhan died. It was the day when the eyes of police officer Ashok Roy, who was used to taking the law into his own hands, fell on Budhan.

CONSTABLE 1: A horrifying act that will force you to ask: are we really free after half a century of independence? Even after all these decades, the British stigma of criminality of birth continues to stick to the DNTs.

CONSTABLE 2: This is an attempt to present the police atrocity that Budhan Sabar had to face.

## Scene Two

(*The actors stand to take the form of a paan shop.* BUDHAN *walks across the street with his wife* SHYAMALI. *The shop owner calls him.*)

SHOPKEEPER: (*To* BUDHAN) O Budhan! Come, buy some paan.

BUDHAN: (*Looks at the shopkeeper and asks his wife*) Shyamali, would you like some?

(SHYAMALI *gives her assent, shyly trying to hide her face behind the pallu of her sari.* BUDHAN *walks across to the paan shop.*)

BUDHAN: Give me two Banarasi paans.

SHOPKEEPER: I will fix them in a moment. (*A few moments later, after applying kattha to the paan*) O Budhanwa, where are you going?

BUDHAN: Oh! On a long journey. You know my uncle? He is not well. We are going to meet him.

SHOPKEEPER: Convey my regards, won't you? Here, take your paan.

BUDHAN: Here is your money.

(*Just as* BUDHAN *is paying the shopkeeper, a police officer takes hold of his hand. He has been moving around in the market looking for a Sabar whom he can hold responsible for all of his pending theft cases.*)

INSPECTOR ASHOK ROY: (*Catching hold of* BUDHAN*'s collar*) Hey, what's your name?

BUDHAN: (*Frightened*) Budhan Sabar, sir.

INSPECTOR ASHOK ROY: I see, a Sabar! Come to the police station with me.

BUDHAN: But sir, what is my crime?

INSPECTOR ASHOK ROY: You bloody rascal, your greatest crime is that you dared to question the law.

(*The officer pulls* BUDHAN *by the shoulder and throws him down on the pavement.*)

BUDHAN: Sir! What are you doing? I… I was…

INSPECTOR ASHOK ROY: Come to the police station without any arguments or I shall parade you naked through the market. (*Kicks* BUDHAN) Come with me!

BUDHAN: Please don't hit me, sir.

(*Hearing* BUDHAN*'s pleas,* SHYAMALI *rushes to his rescue.*)

SHYAMALI: Budhan! What happened, Budhan? Budhan… Sir, why are you beating him? What has my Budhan done, sir?

INSPECTOR ASHOK ROY: You… who are you?

SHYAMALI: Sir… me? I-I am Shyamali. His wife.

INSPECTOR ASHOK ROY: Oh, his wife! Bitch, wife of a thief. Go away. (*He pushes* SHYAMALI *and she falls to the ground. To the constable.*) Drag him through the market to the police station.

SHYAMALI: (*Shouts*) Budhan!

(*All characters stand motionless for a few moments.*)

## Scene Three

SHYAMALI: Shyamali is a simple, innocent woman.

BUDHAN: Budhan was not even told his crime before he was arrested.

SHYAMALI: It is the code of law that the accused be told his crime before being arrested.

CONSTABLE 1: Budhan's *crime* lay in the fact that he belonged to the Sabar community, which is believed to be a community of thieves.

INSPECTOR ASHOK ROY: But Officer Roy? His law was his rifle. Killing Sabars was just an enjoyable game for him.

CONSTABLE 2: Great! What a large-hearted man he is.

(*The actors assume the form of a police station.*)

## Scene Four

INSPECTOR ASHOK ROY: (*To the constable*) Take him away.

CONSTABLE 2: (*Standing outside the police station*) Salaam, Sir.

INSPECTOR ASHOK ROY: Salaam.

*(The constable locks* BUDHAN *in a lock-up.* OFFICER ROY *places his revolver on the table and, after giving some instructions, goes towards the lock-up where* BUDHAN *is kept.)*

INSPECTOR ASHOK ROY: (*To* BUDHAN) Tell me… where have you hidden the stolen goods?

BUDHAN: (*Frightened*) Sir, I have not stolen anything.

INSPECTOR ASHOK ROY: You son of a bitch—I am well aware that you have not committed any theft. But in the past ten days, seventeen thefts have taken place in this area. How many? Did you hear? Seventeen. I have to prepare the reports of these thefts. Don't you understand?

BUDHAN: But sir, I make baskets and sell them to the cooperative.

INSPECTOR ASHOK ROY: (*Interrupting*) I don't care what you do. You have to confess. After all, why else has the law given us this? (*Showing him the baton*) Come, plead guilty.

(OFFICER ROY *hits* BUDHAN. BUDHAN *cries out in pain.* OFFICER ROY *begins to thrash him brutally. Meanwhile,* SHYAMALI *arrives at the police station searching for* BUDHAN.)

SHYAMALI: (*Trying to enter the police station*) Budhan! Budhan!

CONSTABLE 2: (*Stops* SHYAMALI) Hey, woman, where are you going?

SHYAMALI: (*Pleadingly*) Sir, sir, I want to meet my husband, sir.

CONSTABLE 2: Your husband? Who is he?

SHYAMALI: He… whom the officer brought in a short while ago.

CONSTABLE 2: Oh… him! He's a bloody Sabar. A thief.

SHYAMALI: No, sir. Please do not say that… he is not a thief…. He has not committed any theft. He makes baskets and sells them to the cooperative. He did not commit any theft.

CONSTABLE 2: Whether he has or he hasn't committed a theft will be decided by the police. Understand?

SHYAMALI: But sir, he is everything to me, my husband. Let me meet him.

CONSTABLE 2: If you wish to meet your husband, then do so in the court, not here. Get out of here.

(*The constable pushes* SHYAMALI, *who screams for* BUDHAN.)

SHYAMALI: Budhan! Budhan!

(*Her screams are heard by* OFFICER ROY, *who is hitting* BUDHAN.)

INSPECTOR ASHOK ROY: Who is it? Who is shouting?

(*He comes out.* SHYAMALI *falls at his feet.*)

SHYAMALI: Sir, sir, let my husband go. Sir, he has not done anything wrong.

INSPECTOR ASHOK ROY: (*Looking at* SHYAMALI) You? You have come here, too?

SHYAMALI: (*Pleadingly*) Sir, I beg you to let my husband go. Please, sir.

INSPECTOR ASHOK ROY: (*Kicks* SHYAMALI) Leave the police station or you will also be in for it.

SHYAMALI: (*Angrily*) Kill me. Kill me, too. But please let Budhan go. (*Spreads her pallu in front of* OFFICER ROY) I beg you for the life of my husband.

INSPECTOR ASHOK ROY: This is a police station, not a temple where alms are given. Get lost.

(OFFICER ROY *leaves for an inside room.* SHYAMALI *continues to plead.*)

SHYAMALI: Sir... sir. Leave him, sir. (*A constable prevents her from going inside*) Budhan, Budhan! (SHYAMALI, CONSTABLE I *and* CONSTABLE 3 *address the audience together.*)

CHORUS: The police are thirsty for the blood of Sabars. Who will make them understand that we too are Indians?

**Scene Five**

(*The Barabazaar police station.*)

CONSTABLE 2: Date: 11 February 1998.

(OFFICER ROY *arrives at the police station in the morning.*)

CONSTABLE 2: (*Standing at the gate*) Good morning, sir.

INSPECTOR ASHOK ROY: Good morning.

(*Inside the station.*)

CONSTABLE I: Good morning, sir.

INSPECTOR ASHOK ROY: Good morning. (*To the constable*) Has he confessed?

CONSTABLE I: No, sir.

INSPECTOR ASHOK ROY: Hmm. (*Ponders for a while, then says to the constable*) Follow me.

CONSTABLE 3: Sir, should I record yesterday's date as the day of Budhan Sabar's arrest?

INSPECTOR ASHOK ROY: When will you understand? Do you want to become an inspector or not? Our job is to turn facts into fiction and fiction into facts, yesterday into today and today into yesterday. After all, for what other purpose are these official papers and records? Show today's date as the day of Budhan Sabar's arrest. And take special care that the serial number is not the regular one. Is that clear?

(*The constable nods obediently.* OFFICER ROY *and* CONSTABLE I *go up to the lock-up where* BUDHAN *is gasping like a fish out of water.*)

INSPECTOR ASHOK ROY: (*To* CONSTABLE I) Wake him up.

(*The constable kicks* BUDHAN. *He awakes in agony and asks for water.*)

BUDHAN: Water... water. Someone... please give me water. (*His throat is parched; he finds it difficult to speak.*) My, my throat is dry. Please give me some water.

(*A faint smile appears on* OFFICER ROY'*s face as he sees* BUDHAN'*s agony.*)

INSPECTOR ASHOK ROY: You feel thirsty? You want to drink water? (*To the constable*) Shivlal, bring a bottle of liquor and pour it down his bloody throat.

BUDHAN: (*Scared at the mention of liquor*) Sir, sir, I don't drink. Please have mercy on me.

INSPECTOR ASHOK ROY: Great! You are a Sabar and you don't drink!

(SHIVLAL *brings a bottle of alcohol and gives it to* ASHOK ROY.)

INSPECTOR ASHOK ROY: Open your mouth. (*To the constable*) Block his nose.

BUDHAN: No... Sir... no.

(ASHOK ROY *pours the liquid down* BUDHAN'*s throat. Not used to drinking alcohol,* BUDHAN *begins to cough violently.*)

INSPECTOR ASHOK ROY: Now, not only you but your father will have to accept that you committed the theft.

(*Once again, they thrash the half-conscious* BUDHAN *with their fists, legs and sticks.* BUDHAN *cries out in pain. His pain-stricken cries are heard by* SHYAMALI, *who is sitting outside the station, hungry and thirsty. She is terrified. Once again, she runs towards the station, but the constable stops her.*)

CONSTABLE 2: (*Looking at her sternly*) Hey, woman. You are still here?

SHYAMALI: (*Angrily*) I shall not go without meeting my Budhan.

CONSTABLE 2: Leave, or else… (*Threatens her with his staff*)

SHYAMALI: (*Defies him*) Kill me. Kill me along with Budhan. Anyway, what will I do without him?

CONSTABLE 2: If you wish to die, then drown yourself in the village well. But get out of here.

(*He pushes* SHYAMALI. SHYAMALI *stops the passers-by and entreats them to save her husband. On the other side of the stage,* ASHOK ROY *and* CONSTABLE 1 *beat* BUDHAN *brutally.*)

SHYAMALI: Someone help my husband! These people will kill him. Please help me! Budhan is innocent. He has done no wrong. (*Stops an imaginary man on the street*) Please help me! Those people will kill Budhan. (BUDHAN*'s heart-rending scream is heard from inside the police station.*) See… see how mercilessly they're torturing my Budhan? Brother, please help me. We were just eating paan! Is it a crime to eat paan? Budhan… Budhan!

## Scene Six

(*The actors take the form of a police station.*)

CONSTABLE 2: For three days, from 10 February to 12 February, Budhan was kept in prison without food and water

CONSTABLE 3: Budhan was charged with larceny without a remand order. What kind of a law is this?

SHYAMALI: On 13 February, Sridhar Sabar, another Sabar youth, is brought to the Barabazaar Police station.

## Scene Seven

*(The Barabazaar police station. A constable shoves* SRIDHAR SABAR *into the prison cell. In the opposite cell,* ASHOK ROY *walks around* BUDHAN, *who is lying in a delirious state, repeatedly begging for his life.)*

CONSTABLE 2: (*Pulling* SRIDHAR *by the collar*) Go inside. A bloody Sabar thief. (*Pushes* SRIDHAR *into the cell.*)

SRIDHAR: Sir… Please let me go, sir…

CONSTABLE 2: Shut up. (*Locking the door.*)

BUDHAN: (*In a broken voice*) Sir, please leave me. I will die, sir.

INSPECTOR ASHOK ROY: These Sabars are very hard to crack. It seems he will not give in so easily. We will have to use third degree on him. (*To the guard*) Make arrangements for giving him electric shocks.

CONSTABLE 1: But sir… he might die.

INSPECTOR ASHOK ROY: (*Looking stern*) You do as you are told. It's an order.

*(The guard begins to carry out* OFFICER ROY*'s commands. He forces* BUDHAN *to his knees and ties his hands behind him. He ties the electric belt to* BUDHAN*'s head and turns on the machine.* BUDHAN *begins to tremble. His eyes roll. Saliva drips from his mouth. He is given three electric shocks.* SRIDHAR *looks on from the other cell. His eyes fill with tears. He wants to help* BUDHAN, *but he is powerless.)*

## Scene Eight

CONSTABLE 2: The court has ordered that Budhan be taken into remand from 13 February to 16 February.

SRIDHAR: The legal system which is both blind and deaf, did

not take into account that Budhan had already been in remand.

CONSTABLE 1: The deputy commissioner and the superintendent of police searched Budhan's house, but they failed to find anything but poverty.

INSPECTOR ASHOK ROY: On 13 February, the court released Sridhar Sabar on bail and he was taken to the Purulia jail.

BUDHAN: After three days of remand, the court decided to punish Budhan and he too was taken to the Purulia jail.

CONSTABLE 3: Budhan is moved to the Purulia jail after sunset, which is against the set procedures.

## Scene Nine

(*The actors take the form of Purulia jail. The* ASSISTANT SUPERINTENDENT *takes attendance.* SRIDHAR *is also present among the prisoners.*)

ASSISTANT SUPERINTENDENT: Sridhar.

SRIDHAR: Yes, sir.

(*The* SUPERINTENDENT *marks his presence.*)

ASSISTANT SUPERINTENDENT: Hmm... Kanji.

PRISONER: Yes, sir.

(*The* SUPERINTENDENT *marks his presence in the register. Meanwhile a* GUARD *slowly and gently brings* BUDHAN *to the place where the roll call is being marked. He has been brutally beaten and is unable to walk.*)

GUARD: (*To the* SUPERINTENDENT) Sir, he is a Sabar. He was brought here yesterday evening from the Barabazaar police station.

(*On hearing the name Sabar, the* SUPERINTENDENT*'s face fills with hatred.*)

ASSISTANT SUPERINTENDENT: Hmm… search him.

(*The* GUARD *searches* BUDHAN *but finds nothing.*)

GUARD: There is nothing, sir.

ASSISTANT SUPERINTENDENT: Okay. Make him sit there and continue with your work.

GUARD: But sir, it seems he has been severely beaten and injured. He is unable even to walk steadily and has not been medically examined yet.

ASSISTANT SUPERINTENDENT: (*Showing indifference*) Yes. Okay. Sit him up, and then you may go.

(*The* guard *helps* BUDHAN *into a sitting position and goes away.*)

ASSISTANT SUPERINTENDENT: (*To* BUDHAN) Hey, you. What is your name? (*There is no answer.* BUDHAN *is unable to speak. The* SUPERINTENDENT *is furious at not receiving a reply. He raises his voice.*) I said, what is your name? (*There is still no response from* BUDHAN. *The* SUPERINTENDENT *is now fuming with rage. He goes near* BUDHAN *and shakes him.*) You bastard! Can't you hear? I am asking you something. What is your name?

(BUDHAN *stirs as if disturbed from sleep. He is in a state of trauma, unable to understand what is happening to him. Frightened, he replies with great difficulty.*)

BUDHAN: B-B… u… dhan… Budhan Sabar…

ASSISTANT SUPERINTENDENT: Hmm Budhan Budhan Sabar. (*Marks* BUDHAN*'s presence in the attendance register*) What is your wife's name? (*There is again no response from* BUDHAN. *The* SUPERINTENDENT *raises his voice.*) What is your wife's name?

BUDHAN: (*Scared*) Shyamali.

ASSISTANT SUPERINTENDENT: Any children?

BUDHAN: Budhan.

ASSISTANT SUPERINTENDENT: (*Notes something in the register*) Hmm. Okay. Sridhar, you be the sentry for Gate Number 1 after serving lunch.

SRIDHAR: Yes, sir. (*Exits.*)

ASSISTANT SUPERINTENDENT: Kanji, you clean the toilets.

PRISONER I: Yes, Sir.

(*He also exits.* SRIDHAR *and* KANJI *get busy with their work at the rear of the stage.*)

ASSISTANT SUPERINTENDENT: (*To* BUDHAN) And you… Budhan Sabar… You will sweep the entire prison. Understood?

(*After giving orders, the* SUPERINTENDENT *walks off on his daily round of inspection.* BUDHAN *is badly injured. He gets up with great difficulty and takes the broom in his hand, but because of the severe pain in his body, he is unable to move. He sits on one side of the stage. On seeing him sit down, the guard shouts at him.*)

GUARD: Hey… what are you doing? Why aren't you working?

(*The* SUPERINTENDENT *arrives.*)

ASSISTANT SUPERINTENDENT: What's happening?

GUARD: Sir… he is not working.

ASSISTANT SUPERINTENDENT: These bloody Sabars… they are scoundrels. They will never do an honest day's work; they live by thieving alone. (*Catches hold of* BUDHAN *and pushes his face on the floor*) Thrash him so that he gives up being a parasite. (*The* GUARD *and the* SUPERINTENDENT *beat* BUDHAN *mercilessly. His bones are broken. He can no longer even moan, but the* GUARD *and the* SUPERINTENDENT *continue to beat him like an animal.*)

(*After they finish with* BUDHAN) Lock the rascal in a dark cell where not even a single ray of light can enter. Let him yearn for light. Only then will this Sabar realize the value of hard work.

(*The* GUARD *calls the other prisoners working at the rear of the stage, and together they dump the half-conscious* BUDHAN *in a dark cell.*)

**Scene Ten**

(BUDHAN *lies unconscious for some time.* SRIDHAR *enters the cell to give him milk. The cell is pitch-dark, so* SRIDHAR *has difficulty finding* BUDHAN. *He calls his name.*)

SRIDHAR: B-B… udhan… Budh…an. It's so dark here—I can't even see. (*Places his hands over his eyes*) Budhan, oh Budhan… please make some sound. Where are you?

(SRIDHAR *slowly makes his way forward in the dark.* BUDHAN *is lying semiconscious in a corner of the cell.* SRIDHAR's *feet come into contact with* BUDHAN's. *Suddenly,* BUDHAN *wakes up, as if from a deep and painful sleep, and screams as though someone has inflicted fresh injury on his wounds.*)

BUDHAN: (*As* SRIDHAR *touches him*) Don't hit me. Please don't hurt me. I have not done anything, sir. I am innocent. Please don't beat me. I have not committed any theft… Oh! I have not committed any theft… ah! (BUDHAN *writhes in pain as if someone is beating him mercilessly.* SRIDHAR *tries to soothe him.*)

SRIDHAR: Budhan ... Budhan ... Budhan. I am Sridhar, your friend. (*Holding* BUDHAN) You don't recognize me. Look at me. I am Sridhar.

(*On hearing* SRIDHAR's *name,* BUDHAN *quiets down. He slowly tries to gain control of himself. He narrows his eyes and looks at*

SRIDHAR, *then takes* SRIDHAR's *face in his hands. Once he's sure it is* SRIDHAR *beside him,* BUDHAN *begins to cry uncontrollably.*)

BUDHAN: Sridhar, Sridhar, please save me, Sridhar. These people hit me mercilessly. Sridhar, I have not done anything. I-I… I am innocent… I have not stolen anything… You… you know me. I simply make baskets. Sridhar, I beg you, please save me… or… or these people will kill me… Sridhar.

(*On seeing* BUDHAN *break down,* SRIDHAR *is deeply moved.*)

SRIDHAR: (*Trying to console* BUDHAN) Budhan… please don't lose heart… Everything will be okay.

BUDHAN: (*Sobbing*) Sridhar… I am innocent… Believe me… I am innocent.

SRIDHAR: I know, my friend. You have not done anything wrong. But we belong to the Sabar community. We poor tribals can do nothing to these butchers. But, my friend (*Holding* BUDHAN's *face in his hands*). Do not fear. Nothing will happen to you. I'm here with you. (*Picking up the glass*) Drink this milk. (BUDHAN *refuses to drink the milk.*) Please drink it Budhan. You have not eaten anything in the last few days. (*Brings the glass to* BUDHAN's *lips.* BUDHAN *drinks the milk. As soon as* SRIDHAR *moves to leave,* BUDHAN *clutches his legs.*)

BUDHAN: Please don't leave me… don't go away, Sridhar. I'm very frightened here. These people will kill me. Sridhar… please don't leave me.

(*Reluctantly,* SRIDHAR *frees himself from* BUDHAN's *grip and picks up the glass.*)

SRIDHAR: Please don't worry, Budhan. No harm will come to you. Nothing will happen.

(SRIDHAR *goes away. After he leaves, the loneliness of the cell once again gets to* BUDHAN. *He is extremely frightened. He begins to feel that, along with his body, his mind and spirit have been deeply wounded. His mind is crowded with terrifying thoughts. He has lost control over his body and mind. He feels as if his children are calling out to him in the dark cell.*)

A VOICE IN THE BACKGROUND: Father... father... bring me a bird from the market.

A VOICE IN THE BACKGROUND: And Father, bring sweets for me.

(*On hearing these voices, which are really inside his mind,* BUDHAN *grows restless. He feels a void all around him. His mind is unsteady. In the background, there is a rhythmic call of 'Budhan... Budhan', which is very frightening.* BUDHAN *feels that someone is calling out for him in that dark cell. He looks around hysterically. He is disturbed and feels tremendous physical pain. Four actors, chanting, 'Budhan... Budhan' come and surround him.*

*Suddenly* BUDHAN *writhes in pain, feeling that he is being tormented once again.* BUDHAN *wants to escape from those who want to seize his body and spirit, but the four actors terrify him by moving around him like evil spirits. They frighten* BUDHAN *by chanting like ghosts, and continue to chant with a terrifying intensity.*)

CHORUS: Budhan is a thief.

Accept your crime.

Beat the scoundrel.

Give him electric shocks.

Drive him mad.

The dark cell.

(*Their pitch rises and they move around* BUDHAN *in a circle.*)

CHORUS: Budhan is a thief.

Accept your crime.
Beat the scoundrel.
Give him electric shocks.
Drive him mad.
The dark cell.

*(Their pitch rises and they move around* BUDHAN *in a circle more rapidly now.)*

CHORUS: Budhan is a thief.
Accept your crime.
Beat the scoundrel.
Give him electric shocks.
Drive him mad.
The dark cell.

*(Their pitch rises and they move around* BUDHAN *with frenzied circular movement.)*

*(Suddenly, all become silent.* BUDHAN *is unable to bear this attack on his spirit and thinks he is losing his mind. He feels as if the god of death has taken the form of these four people, who are slowly trying to tear out his heart and seize his soul.)*

CHORUS: *(Reaching out for* BUDHAN*'s heart with their hands)*
Death… death… death.

*(Their voice gradually loses its intensity.* BUDHAN *can no longer bear the physical torture and the mental agony. After a heart-rending shriek, he falls down dead, suddenly free from everything. Everything is quiet—silent. The actors leave the stage)*

## Scene Eleven

(BUDHAN *is dead. His body is lying in the police station. The* SUPERINTENDENT *comes with his colleagues for a medical check-up.)*

ASSISTANT SUPERINTENDENT: (*Entering the dark cell*) Today this Sabar will have to be medically checked. (*On seeing* BUDHAN *lying on the floor*) Wake the bloody guy up.

(*One of the prison officers kicks* BUDHAN. *There is no reaction. The* SUPERINTENDENT *tries to make him sit up, but* BUDHAN *does not respond. The* SUPERINTENDENT *tries to feel his breath and check his pulse. He realizes the body is lifeless and is terrified.*)

ASSISTANT SUPERINTENDENT: Oh… my god. He is dead.

(*All become pale.*)

CONSTABLE 2: Sir. If anyone comes to know about this, we'll be in deep trouble.

ASSISTANT SUPERINTENDENT: Yes. You're right. But... (*Thinks for some time*) From which police station was he brought here?

CONSTABLE 3: Sir, from the Barabazaar police station.

ASSISTANT SUPERINTENDENT: Hmm…

(*After pondering for a while, the* SUPERINTENDENT *moves to the phone that is in a corner and dials a number. On the other side,* OFFICER ROY *is sleeping in the Barabazaar police station. He answers the call.*)

INSPECTOR ASHOK ROY: Hello, Barabazaar police station. May I help you?

ASSISTANT SUPERINTENDENT: Hello. This is the assistant superintendent of the Purulia jail speaking.

INSPECTOR ASHOK ROY: Jai Hind, sir.

ASSISTANT SUPERINTENDENT: May I speak to Inspector Roy?

INSPECTOR ASHOK ROY: Speaking.

ASSISTANT SUPERINTENDENT: Inspector Roy, yesterday, your police station sent an accused to us. Budhan Sabar.

INSPECTOR ASHOK ROY: Yes. So?

ASSISTANT SUPERINTENDENT: For your kind information, he is no more.

(*On hearing this,* OFFICER ROY *suddenly grows alert. He is now somewhat worried.*)

INSPECTOR ASHOK ROY: What are you saying, sir?

ASSISTANT SUPERINTENDENT: Yes. He probably died due to excess torture. The torture may have been inflicted in your lock-up or perhaps in our cell. We are both in the same situation, like two sides of a coin. We now have to think how we can wriggle out of this.

INSPECTOR ASHOK ROY: (*Without any worry now and totally at ease*) What do you suggest I do? What have we always done under such circumstances? Suicide...

Assistant Superintendent: Suicide... (*Both laugh excitedly. The* SUPERINTENDENT *puts down the receiver and goes near* BUDHAN*'s corpse and orders the watchman.*) You! Go to the market quickly and buy a piece of cloth.

(CONSTABLE 3 *brings the cloth. The others hold* BUDHAN*'s body upright while the* SUPERINTENDENT *ties the cloth around* BUDHAN*'s neck, thereby making it look like* BUDHAN *has strangled himself to death.*)

ASSISTANT SUPERINTENDENT: Now nobody can say that his death... bring down his body and hand it over to his relatives.

(BUDHAN*'s body is taken away.*)

## Scene Twelve

(BUDHAN*'s body is lying on the floor.* SHYAMALI *comes running. On seeing* BUDHAN *lying dead, she loses her senses and faints. She cannot believe her husband is dead.*)

SHYAMALI: Budhan... Budhan! What happened, Budhan? Why do you not speak, Budhan? See... open your eyes... I am Shyamali... your Shyamali. Look at me, Budhan... Speak to me, Budhan. Why are you so quiet, Budhan? Why don't you talk to me? Get up, Budhan... you cannot leave me like this... (*On seeing* BUDHAN*'s still body and grasping its meaning,* SHYAMALI *gives a heart-rending shriek and begins to cry inconsolably*) Budhan ... Budhan, you cannot go away, leaving me alone. Oh... someone wake my Budhan! Oh... wake him up! Budhan... Budhan... Take me with you! I... Didn't I tell you these people will kill you? Killed you—they've killed you... they have killed my Budhan...

(SHYAMALI *wails loudly and beats her chest with her hands. She clutches* BUDHAN*'s body and cries her heart out.* OFFICER ROY *and the* ASSISTANT SUPERINTENDENT *arrive.*)

ASSISTANT SUPERINTENDENT: Hey, woman. Your husband strangled himself with a piece of cloth.

INSPECTOR ASHOK ROY: Cremate this body now. And stop this wailing. Prepare for his cremation immediately. Understood?

(OFFICER ROY *and the* ASSISTANT SUPERINTENDENT *leave the house. On seeing them walk away,* SHYAMALI *begins to shout like a wounded tigress.*)

SHYAMALI: Cloth! Budhan had no spare piece of cloth with him... oh... you will go to hell. May your wives become widows and your children orphaned. (*Calling them*) You rascals, come back! You have taken my husband away. (*She breaks down. She goes back near* BUDHAN*'s body.*)

Budhan… these same people have killed you. I will kill them… Budhan.

(SHYAMALI *is crying.* ASHISH, *who is a member of the Kheria Sabar Kalyan Samiti, arrives with a message from Mahasweta Devi.*)

ASHISH: Shyamali, Mahasweta Devi says that Budhan's body should not be cremated at any cost. Bury Budhan's body so that nobody comes to know about this. To fool the police, burn an effigy. Have you understood what I have said? And please do not worry. All of us, the Samiti and the villagers along with Mahasweta Devi, will avenge Budhan's death.

(*The man goes away.* SHYAMALI *gets up slowly to the rhythmic chant of 'Budhan… Budhan' in the background. She digs a hole in the floor of her own house and with a heavy heart buries* BUDHAN. *She then lies down on the ground. On the other side of the stage, there is a public demonstration for justice for* BUDHAN*'s murder.*)

## Scene Thirteen

(*A group of demonstrators take centre stage.*)

VILLAGER 1: Budhan did not commit suicide. He was killed.

CONSTABLE 1: Conduct a post-mortem.

VILLAGER 2: The police have killed Budhan.

VILLAGER 3: Budhan was innocent.

SRIDHAR: We want justice… we want justice.

(*They march in a circle.*)

ALL: We want justice.

VILLAGER 1: Let Budhan's death be investigated. We want…

ALL: Justice!

VILLAGER 2: Stop the injustice on Sabars. We want…

ALL: Justice… We want justice, we want justice!

VILLAGER 1: The people's voice has been heard…

CONSTABLE 1: Justice has finally awakened…

VILLAGER 2: At last the day has arrived…

VILLAGER 3: The day of justice…

(*The actors assume the form of a courtroom.*)

SRIDHAR: Date: 21 July 1998. The Calcutta High Court.

## Scene Fourteen

JUDGE: Order… order! The Court has heard the appeal of Smt Mahasweta Devi, Advocate Pradip Roy and Justice D.K. Basu in the Budhan murder case. The post-mortem reports and the Central Forensic Science Laboratory's report prove that Budhan Sabar did not commit suicide. He was killed. The court orders all police officers involved in this crime suspended. The court directs the government to pay one lakh rupees to the widow of Budhan Sabar as compensation, and hands over the detailed investigation of Budhan Sabar's death to the CBI.

(*After the final judgement, all the actors stand still while* BUDHAN'*s spirit takes front stage.* BUDHAN *addresses the audience.*)

BUDHAN: Finally… now… tell me, what was my crime? Why was I killed? I was only eating paan. Is even eating paan a crime for us? My wife is now a widow… My son is fatherless… What will happen to them now that I'm gone? Was . . . did my crime lie in the fact that I was a Sabar? A DNT?

(*As if along with* BUDHAN, *the entire community of DNTs cries. The actors form a semicircle.*)

## Scene Fifteen

SHYAMALI: The same question—every DNT asks this question. Why are they subjected to such atrocities?

VILLAGER 1: If a DNT commits a crime, is the punishment death?

CONSTABLE 1: No Bhansali was born among the DNTs.

VILLAGER 2: No Harshad Mehta was born among the DNTs.

VILLAGER 3: No DNT is involved in a fodder scam.

SRIDHAR: No DNT is involved in the Bofors scandal.

SHYAMALI: Are we second-class citizens?

ALL: Are we second-class citizens?

Are we second-class citizens?

Are we second-class citizens?

Are we second-class citizens?

Are we second-class citizens?

Are we second-class citizens?

ALL: We need respect.

We need respect.

We need respect.

We need respect.

*(They all form a human chain, each actor with a raised hand.)*

# Contributors

**Bhimrao Jadhav** was born in the Kalyanpur settlement in 1926. In his youth, he formed a mutual aid network in the settlement and became active in the agitation to abolish the Criminal Tribes Act. He also participated in the nationalist independence movement in Solapur district. Jadhav organized the first Criminal Tribes Conference in Pune in 1945, and also formed a National Rehabilitation Committee in 1949. Along with the CTA movement, he was also active in the Harijan Sevak Sangh in 1951. The Boroti School for DNT students, and the Bairaag Ashram were both constructed under his guidance. In 1973, Jadhav became the mayor of Solapur. The government of Maharashtra awarded him the Dalit Mitra Puraskar in 1972, the Sharad Gaurav Puraskar in 1998 and the Jivan Gaurav Puraskar in 2011.

**Chandrakant Puri** was a professor at and director of the Centre for Distance Education, SNDT Women's University. He also held the role of chair professor at the Rajiv Gandhi Centre for Contemporary Studies, University of Mumbai. His research interests included social work, social exclusion, development of Denotified and nomadic tribes, and open and distance education for development. He worked on the National Commission on Nomadic and Denotified

Tribes Expert Committee, conducting needs assessment and impact assessment of development projects. He was awarded the Shabdgandh Puraskar for his Marathi literary work, *Karykartyachi Diary* (*The Diary of an Activist*), in 2018. Chandrakant Puri passed away in 2019.

**Dakxin Bajrange** is an award-winning filmmaker, playwright, director and activist. He is the recipient of a Ford Foundation International Fellowship and holds an MA from Leeds University. In 2002, he was awarded the Bhasha Fellowship and he received the Rajiv Gandhi Fellowship in 2004–05. In 2010, Bajrange won the Mahatma Gandhi Best Creative Writing on Human Rights award from the National Human Rights Commission for his book *Budhan Bolta Hai* (*Budhan Speaks*). He is currently a director at Budhan Theatre. He has directed over fifty television programs, twenty documentary films and ten plays, training thousands of actors. He is the author of many academic articles on theatre and film and currently runs his film company, Nomad Movies Ltd. His feature-length film *Sameer: The Perception* (2017) won several international awards.

**Dhruv Bhatt** is a Gujarati novelist. He received the Gujarat Sahitya Akademi and Gujarati Sahitya Parishad awards for his novel *Sumudrantike* (*Oceanside Blues*, 1993). He was also awarded the Sahitya Akademi Award for *Tatvamasi* (*That Thou Art*, 1998). His other works include *Atarapi* (*Sarmey Walks the Pathless Path*, 2001), *Akoopar* (*The Blue Marble*) and *Timirpanthi* (*The Pilgrims of Darkness,* 2019) which details the everyday life of Denotified tribes in Gujarat. His novels have been translated into Hindi, Marathi, Oriya and English.

Bhatt is also the recipient of the Darshak Award, one of the most esteemed honours in Gujarat.

**Henry Schwarz** is professor emeritus of English at Georgetown University, where he was director of the Program on Justice and Peace from 1999 to 2007. His books include *Writing Cultural History in Colonial and Postcolonial India* (1997) and *Constructing the Criminal Tribe in Colonial India: Acting Like a Thief* (2010) and co-edited volumes *Reading the Shape of the World: Toward an International Cultural Studies* (1996) and *A Companion to Postcolonial Studies* (2000). He has produced four documentary films on underclass culture in India, including "Mahasweta Devi: Witness, Advocate, Writer" (2001) and "Please Don't Beat Me, Sir!" (2011) with Shashwati Talukdar and P. Kerim Freidman. He is co-General Editor of the Wiley *Encyclopedia of Postcolonial Studies* (2017).

**Kalpana Gagdekhar** is an eminent actress on the Gujarati stage, and a founding member of Budhan Theatre. She is well known for her portrayal of Kasturba, the wife of M.K. Gandhi. She has toured around the world with several stage productions.

**Kanji Patel** is a Gujarati poet and novelist who often writes about Adivasi and Denotified communities. His novellas include *Kotar ni Dhar Par (On the Brink of the Ravine*, Nakshatra Trust, 1982), *Dahelu* (Rangdwar, 1989; *The Rear Verandah*, Macmillan India, 1997), *Aadi (Primordial*; Gadyaparva, 2008) and *Bhil ni Bhoin (Land of the Bhils*; Joy Burke Foundation, 2019). *Dero (Encampment*, Rangdwar, 2008) is his short story collection about DNTs. He won the Katha award in 1996 and the Dhumketu prize in 2008 for his short fiction. His activism among the Adivasis and Denotified communities earned the Shivshankar award in 2016. He established the Kaleshwari Mela in 1998 in Mahisagar district to provide a platform for cultural expression to DNTs and Adivasis from across India. He is the editor of *Vahi*, a journal of poetry, ritual, and multilingual expression.

**Kushal Batunge** was born and raised in Chharanagar, Ahmedabad. He graduated from Gujarat University with a degree in English literature, and has been making short documentaries for seven years. He is now making his debut feature-length documentary film, *They Call Her 'Mafia'*, and co-writing a book and video series on the oral history of the Chhara tribe with other members of the community. He is an active member of Budhan Theatre. Along with his documentary work, he has also written and directed commercials for corporate media.

**M. Subba Rao** holds an MA in Social Work, from Dravidian University. With three decades of experience in the development sector as a grass root level organiser, trainer of functionaries from the government and non-government sectors, he has been an active fellow-traveller of tribal movements. He has published several ethnographic studies of fisher folk, Denotified and nomadic tribes.

**Roxy Gagdekhar** is a founding member of Budhan Theatre. After a career in local journalism and earning an MA in Journalism from Ball State University in Indiana, he became a reporter with the new Gujarati language service of the BBC. He has spoken at the United Nations, given lectures in the USA and UK, and toured all over India.

**Rupalee Burke** heads the Department of English at a college in Ahmedabad, Gujarat. She has been an active translator for the last three decades, with her works appearing in *Indian Literature, Cordite Poetry Review, Asymptote, Yapanchitra, ChoreoMag, Adivasi Sahitya* and *Vahi* (which she co-edits). Her translations of the oral works of the Koli, Vankar and Bhangi women of the Bhil region formed the basis of the book *The Silken Swing: The Cultural Universe of Dalit Women* (2000). Burke has also translated Girish Karnad's play *Talé-danda* as *Shiraccheda* (2003), and Hansda Sowvendra Shekhar's collection of short stories *The Adivasi Will Not Dance* as *Adivasi Nachashey Nahi* (2018) from English into Gujarati. She is co-editor of *Contemporary Adivasi Writings in India: Shifting Paradigms* (2018).

**Sonal** began working with Adivasi and the Denotified and Nomadic Communities after a university education in literature. She holds a PhD from CEPT University, Ahmedabad. Her research explored the notion of freedom and its evolution and expression in the socio-political movements and imaginative writings of Denotified Communities. Her experience is inter-disciplinary, spanning arts and culture, education, livelihoods, development and human rights.

**Vishal Bhadani** holds a PhD in English and has taught literature at a number of universities in Gujarat. He has translated several novels from Gujarati into English including *The Pilgrims of Darkness* (2015) and *The Blue Marble* by Dhruv Bhatt. He has also translated the biographies of Zandu Bhatt and Maharaja Sayajirao Gaekwad. Bhadani trains teachers across the country on learning and artificial intelligence.

He writes textbooks, translations and reviews for the Government of Gujarat. He co-authored a textbook, *Monsoon: English for Everyone.* He is the director of the International Centre for Applied Gandhian Studies in Gujarat.

## Copyright acknowledgments

The editors and the publisher are grateful for the permission granted to use the following material:

Dakxin Bajrange, excerpts from *Budhan Bolta Hai*, translated by Sonal, original Hindi text copyright Dakxin Bajrange, translation copyright Sonal, courtesy Bhasha Research and Publication Centre, Vadodara, 2010.

Dakxin Bajrange, "Bulldozer", translated by Sonal, original Hindi text copyright Dakxin Bajrange, translation copyright Sonal.

Kushal Batunge, "Who am I?", courtesy of Kushal Batunge

M. Subba Rao, "The life, livelihood and aspirations of a DNT couple", courtesy of M. Subba Rao.

Bhimrao Jadhav, "The story of a hero who broke the fence…", translated by Chandrakant Puri, original Marathi text copyright Bhimrao Jadhav, translation copyright Chandrakant Puri, from *Katha Kateri Kumpanachi*, Chandrakala Prakashan, Pune, 1998; courtesy of Bharat Jadhav.

Kanji Patel and Rupalee Burke. "Pata", translated by Rupalee Burke, original Gujarati text copyright Kanji Patel, translation copyright Rupalee Burke.

Dhruv Bhatt. "Children of Darkness", translated by Vishal Bhadani, original Gujarati text copyright Dhruv Bhatt, translation copyright Vishal Bhadani, excerpt from

*Timirpanthi*, Vedant Publications, Ahmedabad, 2015; courtesy of Arjun Dave.

Kalpana Gagdekhar, "Confessions of a Chhara Actress", translated by Roxy Gagdekhar, original Bhantu text copyright Kalpana Gagdekhar, translation copyright Roxy Gagdekhar.

Dakxin Bajrange, "Budhan", translated by Sonal, original Gujarati text copyright Dakxin Bajrange, translation copyright Sonal, first appeared in G.N. Devy ed., *Painted Words: An Anthology of Tribal Literature*, Orient Longman, New Delhi: 2002; courtesy of Orient Longman.

*Every effort has been made to trace copyright holders and obtain permission; any inadvertent omissions brought to our attention will be remedied in future editions.*